NELSON
English

GRADE **8**

NELSON

NELSON

TABLE OF CONTENTS

WORK WITH VOCABULARY

Words are the basic units of meaning. When we learn how to use words, we are learning how to describe the world around us. If you pay attention to the meaning each word can have, you will notice that most words can mean different things, depending on how they are used.

Taking one word and combining it with others, or adding or removing parts, can have interesting effects. For example, consider the word *scene*. Now think about the meanings of *scenic, obscene, scenery,* and *causing a scene* and notice how they communicate different meanings and feelings. When good writers choose their words carefully, they give their readers a clear picture or feeling.

In this section, you will learn how to use words to write exactly what you mean.

"The difference between the almost right word and the right word is really a large matter—it's the difference between the lightning bug and the lightning."

— Mark Twain

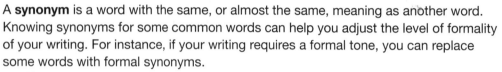

USE A SIMILAR WORD: SYNONYMS

A **synonym** is a word with the same, or almost the same, meaning as another word. Knowing synonyms for some common words can help you adjust the level of formality of your writing. For instance, if your writing requires a formal tone, you can replace some words with formal synonyms.

For example: The creation of our country had both *good* and *bad* effects on its inhabitants.

The creation of our country had both *positive* and *negative* effects on its inhabitants.

In the example, the words *good* and *bad* do not match the formal tone of the rest of the sentence. You can replace them with synonyms, such as *positive* and *negative*, to raise the level of formality.

A. **Complete each sentence by writing a synonym for the word in parentheses ( ).**

1. Let us (start) _Begin_ these proceedings by welcoming the visiting ambassadors.

2. Today, we will (try) _attempt_ to resolve several issues concerning land use.

3. Our government agrees to (buy) _Purchase_ this territory on the following conditions.

B. **For each sentence, decide which of the two synonyms provided has a more formal tone. Circle your choice.**

1. The new country of Canada negotiated several (deals / (treaties)) with Indigenous peoples.

2. One result of these agreements was the ((transfer) / passing) of large areas of land to the Canadian government.

3. The agreements also (gave / (granted)) the government the opportunity to share resources from the land.

C. **Rewrite each sentence, replacing the underlined word(s) with a formal synonym. You may use a thesaurus to help you.**

1. Workers <u>set up</u> labour unions to protect their rights.

   Workers created labour unions to protect their rights

2. In 1960, Indigenous women <u>got</u> the right to vote in federal elections.

   in 1960, Indigenous women were granted the right to vote in federal elections

D. **Write a paragraph about a current Canadian issue in an informal voice. Rewrite the informal paragraph in a more formal voice. Circle the synonyms you used to achieve the more formal voice.**

USE THE OPPOSITE WORD: ANTONYMS

An **antonym** is a word that means the opposite of another word. Knowing the antonyms for some of the words you use is an effective way to make your writing more varied. Some words have absolute antonyms.

For example: The words *present* and *absent* are absolute antonyms—you are either present or absent. There is nothing in between these two states.

Some words do not have absolute antonyms. The antonym for *hot* is not necessarily *cold*, for instance. There are several words that describe states in between hot and cold, such as *cool* and *lukewarm*. The context of your sentence will determine which word you should use.

A. **The words listed below are all possible antonyms for the word *heavy*. Fill in each blank with the appropriate word, based on the context of the sentence.**

light   weightless   fluffy

My mom and dad were carrying all the heavy boxes to the moving truck, so my little sister

and I started carrying the others. I gave her a box of stuffed animals because it was fairly

____light____. I carried a box filled with ___fluffy___ pillows. The next box

felt ___weightless___, and I realized there was nothing in it! Eventually, the four of us got

everything moved out of the house.

B. **Each sentence contains a pair of underlined antonyms. Complete each sentence with a word that means something *in between* the meanings of the antonyms.**

   1. Marie didn't <u>love</u> or <u>hate</u> the idea; her reaction was _____.

   2. I don't want an <u>expensive</u> coat, but I don't want a <u>cheap</u> one, either; I want one that is

   _____.

   3. The stranger wasn't exactly <u>young</u>, but I wouldn't say he was <u>old</u>; he was _____.

C. **For each word, write three antonyms.**

   1. beautiful: _____

   2. boring: _____

   3. small: _____

D. **Choose a pair of antonyms, such as *short* and *tall* or *wet* and *dry*, and list as many words as you can that mean something in between the two. Use a thesaurus to help you. Then, write a paragraph using at least two of the words you found.**

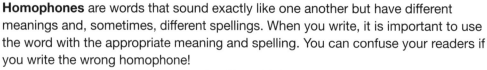

CHOOSE THE CORRECT SPELLING: HOMOPHONES

Homophones are words that sound exactly like one another but have different meanings and, sometimes, different spellings. When you write, it is important to use the word with the appropriate meaning and spelling. You can confuse your readers if you write the wrong homophone!

For example: The café was so loud I couldn't *hear* myself think. ✓

The café was so loud I couldn't *here* myself think. ✗

There are several tricks you can learn to remember which homophone to use when. For instance, we hear with our *ear*, so if the sentence is about listening, use the homophone *hear*. But if the sentence is about a place, use the homophone *here*, which is also in *there*.

You can even make up your own memory tricks to keep your homophones straight!

A. **Each sentence contains a word that has a homophone. Underline the word, and then write the homophone on the line beside the sentence.**

1. I write with my wrist. _____

2. If you are fourth, you are number four. _____

3. It's wonderful that we won! _____

4. Meat is something you eat. _____

B. **Complete the following sentences by choosing the correct homophones and writing them on the short lines. Then, write a memory trick that will help you remember which homophone to choose in the future.**

1. Yan (sent / scent) _____ a message to Ashley saying he was sorry for offending her.

TRICK: _____

2. Shereeka wanted desperately to make (piece / peace) _____ with her best friend.

TRICK: _____

3. They can't send us a postcard from Cuba because (there / they're / their) _____

not (there / they're / their) _____ yet.

TRICK: _____

C. **Choose one of the three homophone sets from the choices below. Write one or two sentences, using all the homophones in the set.**

break / brake   weather / whether   two / to / too

_____

_____

D. **Write one or more descriptive paragraphs using one of the sentences from Exercise B as a starting point. Choose another set of homophones from Exercise A, B, or C, and use them in your writing, too. Underline each homophone.**

_____

_____

_____

_____

_____

_____

_____

_____

_____

_____

_____

_____

_____

_____

_____

_____

_____

_____

_____

_____

_____

_____

_____

_____

_____

EXPAND YOUR VOCABULARY: ROOT WORDS

Words with many syllables and parts can be a challenge to understand and spell. To expand the number of words you can understand and spell, it helps to know some commonly used **root words**. Most root words are word parts that may or may not stand alone as words. For this reason, you usually add a prefix, suffix, or both to a root word.

For example: The word *artist* has the root word *art*, which means "skill." It also has the suffix *-ist*, which means "one who has, is, or does." So, an artist is one who has skill at something.

Many root words come from other languages.

For example: *form* comes from Latin and means "shape"
man / mani / manu comes from Latin and means "hand"
phot / photo comes from Greek and means "light"

A. **Draw a line from each word on the left to its definition on the right. Use the root word to help you.**

1. uniform   **a)** having a response to light

2. photosensitive   **b)** objects made with human skill

3. artifacts   **c)** cuffs to restrain the hands

4. manacles   **d)** having one shape or look

B. **Read each sentence and decide if it is true or false. Write "True" or "False" on the line provided, and then briefly explain your decision. Use the root word of the underlined word to help you.**

1. <u>Photobiology</u> is the study of how different living things are shaped. _____

_____

2. A <u>manuscript</u> is something written by hand. _____

_____

3. Cake batter that <u>conforms</u> when poured into a pan has been made with skill. _____

_____

C. **Write three more words that contain each root word listed below.**

1. *man / mani / manu*: _____

2. *art*: _____

D. **Look through a dictionary to find three more Latin root words and three more Greek root words.**

UNDERSTAND WORD BEGINNINGS: PREFIXES

A **prefix** is a word part added to the beginning of a base word.

For example: *insignificant* = the prefix *in-* + the base word *significant*

When you add a prefix before a base word, the meaning of that word changes.

For example: The prefix *in-* often means "not." The word *insignificant* means "not significant."

Knowing the meanings of common prefixes can help you understand and write unfamiliar words. The following prefixes can all mean "not":

il- as in *illogical*   *ir-* as in *irresistible*   *mis-* as in *misunderstood*

A. **Make a new word by writing one of the following prefixes in front of each base word listed below:**

il-   in-   ir-   mis-

1. _____ complete

2. _____ regular

3. _____ lead

4. _____ expensive

5. _____ legal

6. _____ credible

7. _____ responsible

8. _____ judge

9. _____ literate

B. **Complete each sentence by adding *il-*, *ir-*, or *mis-* to the base word provided.**

1. Meera had (placed) _____ her phone, even though she was usually very organized.

2. Your handwriting is so bad that this letter to your aunt is almost (legible) _____.

3. Luka wrote well but for some reason always (spelled) _____ the word *definitely*.

4. It was very (responsible) _____ of me to leave my puppy alone with the newspaper.

5. The judge dismissed the evidence because she thought it was (relevant) _____ to the case.

C. **Think of two more words that have the prefix *in-* or *mis-* meaning "not." Write a sentence for each word that clearly shows what the word means.**

_____

_____

D. **Find and define two new prefixes. Write down three words that each prefix could be added to.**

_____

_____

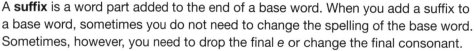
UNDERSTAND WORD ENDINGS: SUFFIXES

A **suffix** is a word part added to the end of a base word. When you add a suffix to a base word, sometimes you do not need to change the spelling of the base word. Sometimes, however, you need to drop the final *e* or change the final consonant.

For example: *argument* = the base word *argue* − the final *e* + the suffix *–ment*
attention = the base word *attend* + change final consonant + the suffix *–tion*

Adding a suffix to the end of a base word can change the meaning of that word. It also usually changes the word's part of speech.

For example: *Argue* is a verb, but when you add the suffix *–ment* to it, it becomes the noun *argument*.

A. **For each word equation, write the correct word.**

1. secure + ity = _____

2. entertain + ment = _____

3. absorb + tion = _____

4. forgive + ness = _____

5. arrive + al = _____

6. endure + ance = _____

B. **Each sentence is missing a noun. Change the verb provided in parentheses into a noun by adding one of the following suffixes:**

-ance   -er   -ation   -or

1. The musicians all stood up as the (conduct) _____ walked across the stage.

2. The orchestra's (combine) _____ of classical and modern music clearly impressed the audience.

3. Every (listen) _____ left the show feeling very satisfied.

4. Four members of the royal family were in (attend) _____ at the concert.

C. **Change each of the verbs into a noun by adding a suffix. Then, write a sentence for each noun that clearly shows what it means.**

confuse: _____   confide: _____

1. _____

2. _____

D. **Look through a few books to find three base words with suffixes. Write two sentences for each word you find: one sentence using the base word with a suffix, and one sentence using the base word without a suffix.**

COMBINE TWO WORDS: CONTRACTIONS

To form a **contraction** when you write, combine two or more words to make a new word. Then, replace one or more of the letters with an apostrophe (') to make the new word shorter.

For example: I *could have* kept running for another kilometre!

I *could've* kept running for another kilometre!

Using contractions when you speak makes your speech sound natural. Likewise, using contractions when you write makes the tone of your writing more informal. An informal tone is especially appropriate when you are writing dialogue (what someone says).

A. **In each sentence, write the words that make up the contraction.**

1. I told Bonnie, "I've (_____ _____) found a great yoga class for Derek."

2. Bonnie said, "He's (_____ _____) never done yoga before!"

3. I commented, "It would've (_____ _____) been helpful when he hurt his back last year."

4. Later, we asked Derek, "How'd (_____ _____) your first yoga class go?"

B. **Rewrite each sentence, replacing two of the words with a contraction.**

1. I should have made sure I had my water bottle before I left the house.

_____

2. Our team is winning, even though we have never played beach volleyball before!

_____

3. Sanjay asked, "Where did Coach Ferguson go?"

_____

4. Rashid answered, "She has gone to talk to the referee."

_____

C. **Turn each pair of words into a contraction, and write a sentence of dialogue using it.**

1. might have: _____

_____

2. why did: _____

_____

D. **Look through a book for a paragraph that uses formal language. Rewrite the paragraph, using contractions. How does using contractions change the tone of the paragraph?**

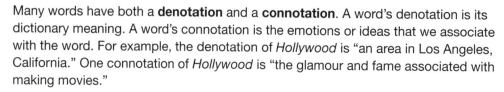

MIND YOUR MEANING: DENOTATION AND CONNOTATION

Many words have both a **denotation** and a **connotation**. A word's denotation is its dictionary meaning. A word's connotation is the emotions or ideas that we associate with the word. For example, the denotation of *Hollywood* is "an area in Los Angeles, California." One connotation of *Hollywood* is "the glamour and fame associated with making movies."

Good writers know both a word's denotation *and* its connotation. They provide context clues so readers will understand which meaning is being used.

For example: She thought the movie role would be her ticket to *Hollywood*.
We drove through *Hollywood* during rush hour.

In the first example, the context clue of "the movie role" tells readers that *Hollywood* is being used to suggest fame. In the second example, the writer has not included any context clues about movies or fame, so readers know that the denotation of *Hollywood* is being used. It is literally the place the writer "drove through."

A. **For each pair of sentences, decide which one uses the denotation of the underlined word and which one uses the connotation. Write *D* or *C* on the line after each sentence.**

1. Everything is coming up <u>roses</u> for Pia today. ___

   The Lees grew three kinds of <u>roses</u> in their front yard. ___

2. The apples were not ready for picking yet; they were still <u>immature</u>. ___

   It was really <u>immature</u> of Lisa to have a temper tantrum at the birthday party. ___

B. **For each word provided, write two sentences on the lines. One sentence should use the word's denotation and one should use a connotation. You may use a dictionary to help you with this exercise.**

1. (low) _____

   _____

   _____

2. (shady) _____

   _____

   _____

3. (heart) _____

   _____

   _____

LESSON 9

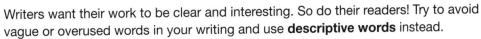

BE CLEAR AND INTERESTING: DESCRIPTIVE WORDS

Writers want their work to be clear and interesting. So do their readers! Try to avoid vague or overused words in your writing and use **descriptive words** instead.

For example: Tomas *said*, "The museum was *nice*."
Tomas *admitted*, "The museum was *wonderful*."

The words *said* and *nice* are very commonly used, and they do not provide clear descriptions of how Tomas spoke or how much he liked the museum. The words *admitted* and *wonderful* are much more descriptive, and they will help readers understand what you are trying to convey. You can use a thesaurus to find descriptive words that mean exactly what you intend to say.

A. **Each sentence contains an underlined word that is vague or overused. Replace it with a more descriptive word.**

1. After eating all of the seeds, the chipmunk <u>went</u> away. _____

2. "I enjoyed that movie," Pooja commented. "Those actors are <u>great</u>!" _____

3. The <u>bad</u> weather continued all week, so Delaney had to postpone her trip. _____

B. **Rewrite each sentence on the line provided, replacing the underlined words with more descriptive words.**

1. I <u>hit</u> the <u>ball</u> and it <u>went</u> through the air.

_____

2. Khalid <u>liked</u> painting and <u>doing</u> sculptures, but he <u>really</u> liked drawing.

_____

C. **Rewrite this text, replacing each instance of the words *good* and *help* with a more descriptive word (making sure that it fits the context of the sentence).**

I think it's *good* to try to *help* people whenever you can. If my friends need *help* with stress, I tell them to listen to music, go for a walk, or talk to a friend. Sometimes a *good* run or bike ride can *help*, too.

_____

_____

_____

_____

_____

D. Write two paragraphs about your likes and dislikes. Use descriptive words. Avoid using vague words.

_____

_____

_____

_____

_____

_____

_____

_____

_____

_____

_____

_____

_____

_____

_____

_____

_____

_____

_____

_____

_____

_____

_____

_____

USE SLANG: INFORMAL AND FORMAL LANGUAGE

Whenever you write, be sure you know your audience (whom you are writing for) and your purpose (why you are writing). This knowledge will help you decide how formal your language should be.

For a history essay, you should use **formal language**. For an email to a friend, you could use **informal language**. Informal language is closer to the way you speak than formal language is. It can include simpler, shorter words, contractions, and slang.

Slang is language used by specific groups, such as teenagers, Canadians, or people who grew up in a certain time period, such as the 2000s. Slang can change over time, and it can differ from region to region.

For example: *square* = 1950s slang for "old-fashioned" or "boring"

bloke = British slang for "man"

Because slang is informal language, it is not usually appropriate in formal writing. Your readers may not understand a slang word or phrase if they belong to a group that does not use it!

A. **Match each slang word on the left with its more formal version on the right.**

bromance   an enemy posing as a friend

chill   a close friendship between two males

frenemy   calm down and relax

B. **In each sentence, underline the slang word or phrase that might not be understood by an audience that does not use it.**

   1. Can I get a double-double and a chocolate doughnut, please?

   2. Marty is such a slacker that I'll be surprised if he gets his project done on time.

   3. All I want to do this weekend is zone out in front of the TV.

   4. Grandpa, sit beside me so we can take a selfie.

C. **Rewrite each sentence, replacing the underlined slang word or phrase with more formal language.**

   1. The marathon runners were completely <u>wiped out</u> by the time they reached the finish line.

   _____

   2. Even the most critical music reviewer must agree that this song is <u>sick</u>.

   _____

D. Write two versions of a short conversation between two people who witnessed an exciting event. In the first version, use informal language and include as many slang words and phrases as you can. Then, rewrite the conversation using more formal language and no slang.

_____

_____

_____

_____

_____

_____

_____

_____

_____

_____

_____

_____

_____

_____

_____

_____

_____

_____

_____

_____

_____

_____

_____

USE VARIETY: LITERARY DEVICES

Writers use many tools to make their work come alive. These tools, called **literary devices**, can help readers visualize what is being described so they understand it better. Literary devices can also cause readers to experience a specific emotion or reaction.

There are many types of literary devices.

For example: *Simile*—a comparison using the words *like* or *as*: "as hard as nails"
Metaphor—a comparison not using the words *like* or *as*: "She has a heart of gold."
Idiom—an expression that is not meant literally: "Get your act together!"
Alliteration—several words with the same beginning consonant sound appearing close together: "Christian cooked coconut crepes."
Personification—the use of human qualities or abilities to describe something non-human: "The kettle sang."
Onomatopoeia—the use of a word that sounds like what it means or that imitates the sound made by a person, animal, or thing: *crash, hum, buzz*.

A. Identify the type of literary device used in each sentence. Find the type in the list underneath the sentence and circle it.

1. The moon is a white balloon.

   a) metaphor

   b) simile

   c) onomatopoeia

2. The tree's leaves dance in the wind.

   a) alliteration

   b) personification

   c) idiom

B. Each sentence uses a literary device to convey an idea. On the shorter line, write the type of literary device used. Then, rewrite the sentence, in your own words.

1. Fatima's hair was as soft as silk. _____

   _____

2. Jared called my name at the top of his lungs. _____

   _____

3. Theo thudded downstairs, thumping thunderously. _____

   _____

4. The tree's heavy branches groaned in the gusts of wind. _____

   _____

C. The following poem uses language that does not engage readers' interest. Rewrite each line using a literary device to convey the same meaning and to spark more interest in your audience. Use the hint at the end of each line to help you.

Celeste said quietly,   (alliteration)

"This old house is full of noises   (onomatopoeia)

and really dark corners.   (simile)

It's making me very scared."   (metaphor)

_____

_____

_____

_____

D. Write your own poem. Try to use as many types of literary devices as you can. Underline each device.

_____

_____

_____

_____

_____

_____

_____

_____

_____

_____

_____

_____

_____

_____

_____

_____

_____

_____

SECTION REVIEW

A. **For each underlined word, write an informal synonym and a formal synonym. You may use a thesaurus to help you.**

	Informal Synonym	Formal Synonym
1. They had a serious <u>talk</u> later that day.	_____	_____
2. This cherry pie is <u>great</u>!	_____	_____
3. Our media project is finally <u>finished</u>!	_____	_____
4. Will you <u>trade</u> seats with me so I can see better?	_____	_____
5. My dad looks very <u>comfortable</u> in his armchair.	_____	_____

B. **Complete the scale by writing antonyms for the word *bad*. Use the following sentence to help you determine the context of *bad*. You may use a thesaurus to help you.**

I expected the cafeteria food to taste OK, but it was *bad*.

good _____ _____ _____ **scrumptious**

C. **Each sentence provides a trick to help you remember how to use the pair of homophones in parentheses correctly. Complete each sentence by writing the correct homophone.**

1. If something is _____, then it isn't t<u>here</u>. (here / hear)

2. A _____ is a h<u>ard</u> piece of wood. (bored / board)

3. The opposite of a _____ is an <u>i</u>nsult. (compliment / complement)

4. The baby's _____ was <u>eight</u> pounds. (wait / weight)

5. Have another _____ of p<u>ie</u>! (piece / peace)

D. **Each word contains the root word *art*, which means "skill." Use each word in a sentence; use the meaning of the root word to help you. You may also use a dictionary.**

1. artist: _____

_____

2. artifact: _____

_____

3. artisan: _____

_____

4. artificial: _____

_____

E. Form a new word from each base word by adding one of the listed prefixes or suffixes. Write the new words, changing the spelling of the base word if necessary. Not all prefixes and suffixes will be used.

Prefixes	Base Words	Suffixes	New Words
il–	logical	-ness	_____
in–	entertain	-ance / ence	_____
mis–	conduct	-ment	_____
ir–	drowsy	-tion / ation / ion	_____
non–	persevere	-er / or	_____

F. Write two answers to the following question, one using contractions and the other spelling out the complete words:

Have you ever thought about what might have happened if we had found creatures on the Moon?

Answer 1: _____

_____

Answer 2: _____

_____

G. Read the sentence below. Write the denotation and connotation of the underlined word.

Carly knows a lot of people because she's such a social <u>butterfly</u>.

denotation: _____

connotation: _____

H. The following sentences contain underlined examples of literary devices. After each sentence, write the type of literary device used and then explain what it means. Choose from the following types of literary devices:

simile   metaphor   idiom   personification

1. In this heat wave, that water fountain is <u>a sight for sore eyes</u>. _____

_____

2. Even though Petal's camera was <u>a dinosaur</u>, it took great pictures. _____

_____

3. The fire <u>leapt</u> across the stream, heading toward the forest. _____

_____

4. The lineup for the roller coaster was moving <u>like a snail</u>. _____

_____

I. **Write two paragraphs describing your favourite book or movie. Explain why you like it and why someone else might want to read or see it. Use at least six descriptive words; try to avoid vague and overused words. Circle the descriptive words you used.**

_____

_____

_____

_____

_____

_____

_____

_____

_____

_____

_____

_____

_____

_____

_____

_____

_____

_____

_____

_____

_____

_____

_____

J. **Write an email to someone who does not understand the slang you and your friends use. In the email, list some slang expressions and explain what they mean in more formal language.**

_____

_____

_____

_____

_____

_____

_____

_____

_____

_____

_____

_____

_____

_____

_____

_____

_____

_____

_____

_____

_____

_____

_____

_____

_____

_____

_____

BUILD SENTENCES

Sentences are where *things* and *actions* meet to make a complete idea. Each sentence is a tiny story in itself—nouns (or subjects) are the characters, and verbs (or predicates) are the plots.

In good writing, every sentence should have a reason for being there. Every sentence should have a purpose, whether it is to describe a scene, explain details, make a point, or make the readers feel an emotion.

In this section, you will learn how to put together perfect sentences.

"Every word you add dilutes the sentence."

— Miller Williams

USE VARIETY: TYPES OF SENTENCES

There are four **types of sentences**: declarative (makes a statement), imperative (makes a command), interrogative (asks a question), and exclamatory (makes an exclamation).

For example: I run five kilometres every day. (statement)
Stretch before you run. (command)
How far do you run every day? (question)
I love running! (exclamation)

Each type of sentence requires specific punctuation. A statement or a command ends with a period (although a command can sometimes end with an exclamation mark). A question ends with a question mark, and an exclamation ends with an exclamation mark.

Use different sentence types for different purposes and audiences. For example, commands are effective if you are writing instructions. Questions are often used in dialogue or to directly address readers. Exclamations express strong emotion.

A. Add end punctuation to each sentence. Write the sentence type (declarative, imperative, interrogative, or exclamatory) on the line beside each sentence.

   1. I have to do exercises every day to help my ankle heal____ _____

   2. Take your shoes off at the door____ _____

   3. What a cool idea____ _____

   4. Help me think of an April Fool's prank for my dad____ _____

   5. Did you watch the video I sent you____ _____

   6. Corinne's face went red when the teacher caught her texting in class____ _____

   7. You were supposed to pick me up an hour ago____ _____

   8. Do you know how to make a wampum belt____ _____

B. Write a description of a cultural event you have experienced or would like to attend in your community. Include at least one example of each sentence type.

   _____

   _____

   _____

   _____

   _____

   _____

   _____

C. Write a short dialogue between two people discussing the pros and cons of leading an active lifestyle. Use a variety of sentence types.

_____

_____

_____

_____

_____

_____

_____

_____

_____

_____

_____

_____

_____

_____

_____

_____

_____

_____

_____

_____

_____

_____

_____

_____

USE VARIETY: SENTENCE LENGTH

If you have too many sentences of the same length, your writing may be dull and repetitive. To keep your readers interested, **vary the lengths of your sentences**.

Use a variety of short, medium, and long sentences. Long, descriptive sentences can help readers picture what you are writing about or give them details about your topic. Short sentences can be used to grab readers' attention or to show surprise or excitement. Using a variety of sentence lengths can bring your writing to life and make it flow more smoothly.

A. **Rewrite this paragraph, using a variety of short and long sentence lengths.**

Dominic stepped up to the bat and remembered that his sister had told him to keep his eye on the ball. He was nervous and his heart was beating fast, so he took a deep breath and lifted the bat. Dominic watched the ball and swung the bat and hit the ball with a whack and, after that, he started to run.

_____

_____

_____

_____

_____

_____

_____

B. **Write a paragraph about how you reacted or might react in an emergency situation. Use a variety of short, medium, and long sentences.**

_____

_____

_____

_____

_____

_____

_____

_____

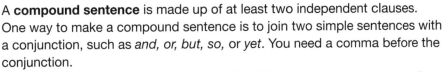

COMBINE SENTENCES: COMPOUND SENTENCES

A **compound sentence** is made up of at least two independent clauses. One way to make a compound sentence is to join two simple sentences with a conjunction, such as *and, or, but, so,* or *yet*. You need a comma before the conjunction.

> For example: The weather was terrible. They cancelled soccer practice.
> The weather was terrible, so they cancelled soccer practice.

You can also use a semicolon to combine two independent clauses.

> For example: The weather was terrible; they cancelled soccer practice.

You can use compound sentences to link related ideas or to vary the length of your sentences. Compound sentences can make your writing more interesting for readers.

A. Underline the compound sentences in this paragraph.

Have you ever felt like an alien in your own school? When I first moved here, that's exactly how I felt. It was the middle of the school year, and everyone had already formed groups of friends. They all stared at me as I walked down the hall, like I was an unwelcome intruder from another planet. After a while, things started to get better. People started to call me by my name; they stopped saying, "Hey, New Girl." I decided that the best way to make friends was to get involved in activities that I was interested in, so I joined the school band, auditioned for the school play, and tried out for the girls' basketball team. I figured that, among the three groups, there had to be some people who would let an alien sit with them at lunch.

B. Write three compound sentences about healthy living. Use a conjunction or semicolon in each sentence.

1. _____

_____

_____

2. _____

_____

_____

3. _____

_____

_____

EXPAND SENTENCES: ADDING DETAILS

Writers expand simple sentences by **adding details** that give a clear picture of what they are writing about. Readers stay more interested if they can sense the who, what, where, when, why, or how of a sentence. You can add details by using an adjective, adverb, adjective phrase, or adverb phrase. An adjective phrase consists of more than one word and functions as an adjective. An adverb phrase consists of more than one word and functions as an adverb.

For example: The *talented* (adjective) girl danced *quickly*. (adverb)
The *very talented* (adjective phrase) girl danced *as quickly as possible*. (adverb phrase)

Expanding sentences also helps you vary their length so your sentences do not all sound the same.

A. Read the paragraph below. Expand the sentences by adding at least one adjective, adjective phrase, adverb, and adverb phrase.

Our teacher is funny. Today, he did an impression of a velociraptor. He bobbed his head and walked around the classroom. We all laughed. Then, we all did impressions of dinosaurs.

_____

_____

_____

_____

B. Write a descriptive paragraph about the funniest person you know.

_____

_____

_____

_____

_____

_____

_____

_____

EDIT SENTENCES: RUN-ON SENTENCES

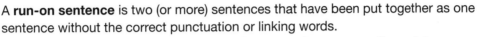

A **run-on sentence** is two (or more) sentences that have been put together as one sentence without the correct punctuation or linking words.

For example: I waited until the last minute to write my essay it was late.

There are different ways for fixing run-on sentences: 1) make two separate sentences; 2) use a comma and a conjunction (*and, or, but, so,* or *yet*) to make a compound sentence; 3) use a semicolon to make a compound sentence.

For example: I waited until the last minute to write my essay. It was late.
I waited until the last minute to write my essay, so it was late.
I waited until the last minute to write my essay; it was late.

You can avoid run-on sentences as you write by being aware of the parts of your sentences. Also, read your writing to yourself, using your punctuation as a guide. If your sentence should have a pause but there is no punctuation to suggest one, you might have a run-on sentence.

A. Underline the run-on sentences in this paragraph.

The worst part about spraining my wrist is that I can't practise my violin. I have been playing the violin since I was six it is my favourite thing to do. Also, I need to practise for the spring recital. We have been rehearsing for weeks this is a major setback. To keep myself from getting too stressed, I am focusing on my recovery and practising my part in my head.

B. Correct these run-on sentences.

1. The soccer coach was very strict Darren always made sure he arrived at practice on time.

_____

_____

_____

2. Mikaela has known since she was six that she wants to be a doctor I have no idea what career I want.

_____

_____

_____

3. Peta pressured me to jump off the cliff into the water I was too scared.

_____

_____

_____

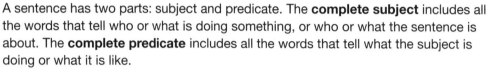

KNOW COMPLETE SUBJECTS AND PREDICATES

A sentence has two parts: subject and predicate. The **complete subject** includes all the words that tell who or what is doing something, or who or what the sentence is about. The **complete predicate** includes all the words that tell what the subject is doing or what it is like.

For example: The football team ran three laps around the field.
Complete subject: *the football team*
Complete predicate: *ran three laps around the field*

Being aware of complete subjects and complete predicates helps you understand how your sentences fit together when you write.

A. Underline the complete subject and circle the complete predicate in each sentence.

1. A heated debate about environmental issues started in science class today.

2. Many of the city's residents have been disappointed with the new mayor's transportation policies.

3. One of the students in my gym class fainted from heat stroke this afternoon.

4. The school band will perform at the seniors' residence on Monday.

5. Over half of the students in class voted in favour of working outside this afternoon.

6. Where did you put my bag?

7. My brother taught me the Rabbit Dance for the powwow next week.

B. Write a complete predicate for each complete subject.

1. The marathon runner _____

2. An unlikely guest _____

3. My favourite flower _____

4. Too many people _____

5. My friends and I _____

C. Write two sentences about volunteering. Underline the complete subject and circle the complete predicate in each sentence.

1. _____

   _____

2. _____

   _____

D. Write two paragraphs about a piece of modern technology you would take to a desert island. Explain your reasons. Use adjectives and adverbs.

_____

_____

_____

_____

_____

_____

_____

_____

_____

_____

_____

_____

_____

_____

_____

_____

_____

_____

_____

_____

_____

_____

_____

_____

_____

_____

_____

IDENTIFY WHO OR WHAT: SIMPLE SUBJECTS

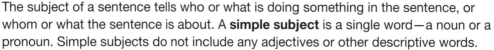

The subject of a sentence tells who or what is doing something in the sentence, or whom or what the sentence is about. A **simple subject** is a single word—a noun or a pronoun. Simple subjects do not include any adjectives or other descriptive words.

For example: My mother's tried-and-true *method* for managing stress is daily physical activity.

In the example, *method* is the simple subject. Notice that it does not include *my mother's tried-and-true* or *for managing stress*, which are all part of the complete subject.

A. **Underline the simple subject in each sentence.**

1. Stephan's fancy new phone is a lot nicer than mine.

2. The first day of school is always an adjustment after having the entire summer off.

3. Locally grown organic food is becoming more and more popular in my community.

4. Emilie's greatest achievement this year was becoming student council president.

5. The best advice my grandmother gave me was to enjoy each day to the fullest.

6. Luciana's ultimate goal is to become an investigative journalist.

B. **Choose a writing topic from the list below. Write a paragraph about the topic. Then, circle the simple subject in each sentence of your paragraph.**

What is your ideal holiday?   What makes music good?   What are your personal talents?

_____

_____

_____

_____

_____

_____

_____

_____

_____

C. **Write one question, one statement, and one exclamation. Circle the simple subject in each sentence.**

IDENTIFY THE ACTION: SIMPLE PREDICATES

A **simple predicate** contains only the verb from the action part of a sentence. Simple predicates do not include any adverbs or other descriptive words.

For example: Kayla and Aaron *ran* as fast as they could to the bus stop.

In the example, *ran* is the simple predicate. Notice that it does not include the descriptors *as fast as they could* or *to the bus stop,* which are all part of the complete predicate.

A simple predicate can sometimes be more than one word. Some verb forms are several words long.

For example: The wild cat *was stalking* her prey slowly and stealthily.
Misha *might have arrived* at the party before everyone else.

A. Underline the simple predicate in each sentence.

1. I run for twenty minutes every day, rain or shine.

2. Our dog is escaping through the broken gate.

3. I am writing a letter to the city councillor about the lack of recycling bins in public spaces.

4. Kassina walked sluggishly down the stairs for breakfast.

5. The audience applauded wildly as the actors took their bows.

6. The animal shelter is hiring dog walkers and cat sitters.

7. Marco will be going to the gym this afternoon.

8. Many people in my community have become interested in urban gardening.

B. Choose three topics from the following list. Write a sentence about each topic. Then, underline the simple predicate in each sentence.

sports safety   imagination   Canada   cyberbullying   vacations

1. _____

_____

2. _____

_____

3. _____

_____

C. Choose one of the sentences you wrote for Exercise B. Write a paragraph using the sentence as your opening line. Underline the simple predicate in each sentence.

IDENTIFY WHO OR WHAT: COMPOUND SUBJECTS

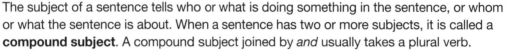

The subject of a sentence tells who or what is doing something in the sentence, or whom or what the sentence is about. When a sentence has two or more subjects, it is called a **compound subject**. A compound subject joined by *and* usually takes a plural verb.

For example: A *tree* and a *bush* stand beside the house.

In the example, the two subjects, *tree* and *bush*, form a compound subject and take a plural verb, *stand*.

A. **In each sentence, decide if there is a compound subject. If there is, underline the compound subject.**

1. My aunt and uncle are coming over for dinner tonight.

2. The racoon gets into the compost almost every night.

3. Jamal's hockey stick and helmet need to be replaced this year.

4. After the storm, the grocery store and the pharmacy had to close due to flood damage.

B. **Underline the compound subject in each sentence. Then, choose the verb in parentheses that agrees with the subject and write it on the line.**

1. China, India, and Thailand _____ countries I want to visit someday. (are / is)

2. Serena and Brent _____ choir practice every Wednesday night. (have / has)

3. My brother and sister _____ me when I'm trying to study. (bother / bothers)

4. A pillow and a sleeping bag _____ all I need for the sleepover. (are / is)

C. **Write three sentences, using a compound subject in each one. Choose one of the topics from the list below or think of a topic of your own.**

space travel   competitive sports   natural disasters   healthy eating

1. _____

_____

2. _____

_____

3. _____

_____

D. **Underline the compound subject in each of your sentences in Exercise C. Circle the plural verb that matches it.**

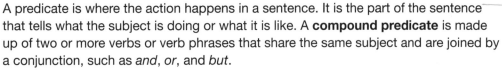

IDENTIFY THE ACTION: COMPOUND PREDICATES

A predicate is where the action happens in a sentence. It is the part of the sentence that tells what the subject is doing or what it is like. A **compound predicate** is made up of two or more verbs or verb phrases that share the same subject and are joined by a conjunction, such as *and*, *or*, and *but*.

For example: After dinner, Sanjeev *finished* his homework and *listened* to music.

In the example, the words *finished* and *listened* together form the compound predicate. They share the same subject, *Sanjeev*, and are joined by the conjunction *and*.

To find the compound predicate, ask what the subject does or is. For example, what did Sanjeev do? He *finished* his homework and *listened* to music.

A. **Decide if each sentence uses a compound predicate. If it does, underline the subject and circle the compound predicate.**

1. My grandmother lives around the corner and drives a red car.

2. Sabrina went to the gym in the afternoon and in the evening.

3. The girls walk or bike to school every day.

4. Oscar's father gives good advice and is easygoing.

5. The cleaners mopped the floors and wiped the counters.

6. In the morning, I eat cereal or eggs.

B. **Write three sentences with compound predicates, using the subject and verbs provided.**

Subject: soccer team   **Verbs:** played, lost

1. _____

_____

Subject: I   **Verbs:** went, saw

2. _____

_____

Subject: Hamed's older brother   **Verbs:** drove, bought

3. _____

_____

C. **Write a definition for *compound predicate* in your own words.**

UNDERSTAND COMPOUND SUBJECTS AND PREDICATES

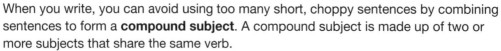

When you write, you can avoid using too many short, choppy sentences by combining sentences to form a **compound subject**. A compound subject is made up of two or more subjects that share the same verb.

For example: *Portia* bikes to school. *Bob* bikes to school.

Portia and *Bob* bike to school. (two subjects + one verb)

Subjects joined by *and* usually take a plural verb, such as *bike* in this example.

You can also combine sentences to form a compound predicate. A **compound predicate** is made up of two or more verbs or verb phrases that share the same subject. The verbs or verb phrases are joined by a conjunction, such as *and*, *or*, and *but*.

For example: The car slowed down. It did not stop.

The car *slowed* down but *did not stop*. (one subject + two verbs)

A. **Underline the compound subject or predicate in each sentence. Then, on the short line, write *CS* for compound subject or *CP* for compound predicate.**

1. Karyn looked at her brother and smiled. _____

2. The dishes and the laundry need to be put away. _____

3. Angie went to soccer practice but didn't play. _____

4. My arms and legs are sore from track and field practice. _____

5. Odin was getting tired but wouldn't sleep. _____

6. Hari jumped in the lake and swam out to the floating dock. _____

B. **Combine each pair of sentences by creating a compound subject or compound predicate. Rewrite each sentence.**

1. Louis took out his pencil. He started writing.

_____

2. Paolo follows the lifeguard's instructions closely. Mina does, too.

_____

3. The clinic is closed today. The pharmacy is also closed today.

_____

C. **Write one sentence with a compound subject and one sentence with a compound predicate. Then, rewrite each of your sentences as two separate sentences. Which version do you prefer?**

IDENTIFY SENTENCE PARTS: DIRECT AND INDIRECT OBJECTS

An object is a noun or pronoun that receives the action in a sentence. There are two kinds of objects: **direct objects** and **indirect objects**.

A direct object receives the direct action of a verb. One way to find the direct object in a sentence is to follow this formula: subject + verb + what / whom ?

For example: Shawna played the piano.

In this example, *Shawna* is the subject (the one doing the action) and *played* is the verb (the action). What did Shawna play? *The piano*. That is the direct object.

An indirect object is the person or thing that is having the action done to (or for) them. An indirect object cannot exist without a direct object.

For example: Shawna played a song for her mother.
Shawna played her mother a song.

In both examples, *a song* is the direct object. For whom did Shawna play a song? For *her mother*. Therefore, *her mother* is the indirect object. As the examples show, the indirect object can appear before or after the direct object. If it appears after, it is introduced by the preposition *to* or *for*.

A. **Read each sentence and decide whether the underlined word is a direct or an indirect object. Write *D* for direct or *I* for indirect.**

1. Leticia passed <u>a note</u> to her friend in science class. _____

2. My teacher offered <u>me</u> a second chance to write the exam. _____

3. The baseball team gave <u>their fans</u> a good show today. _____

4. Caleb wished me <u>luck</u> on my audition for the school play. _____

5. I lent <u>Emma</u> my phone because hers was broken. _____

6. I showed <u>the report card</u> to my parents with hesitation. _____

B. **Write two sentences about what leadership means to you. Use direct and indirect objects in your sentences.**

_____

_____

_____

_____

_____

RECOGNIZE INDEPENDENT AND SUBORDINATE CLAUSES

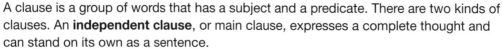

A clause is a group of words that has a subject and a predicate. There are two kinds of clauses. An **independent clause**, or main clause, expresses a complete thought and can stand on its own as a sentence.

For example: Owen is learning how to cook.

A **subordinate clause** cannot stand on its own as a sentence; it depends on an independent clause to make sense.

For example: because he wants to become a chef

Subordinate clauses are important because they add information. A subordinate clause usually begins with a conjunction, such as *after*, *before*, *because*, *whenever*, *even though*, *rather than*, *although*, *as soon as*, or *as long as*. You can place a subordinate clause before or after an independent clause. If you put it before the independent clause, the subordinate clause should be followed with a comma.

A. **For each sentence, underline the independent clause once and the subordinate clause twice. Circle the conjunction that introduces the subordinate clause.**

1. Before I go for a run, I always make sure to do some stretches.

2. We decided to buy our movie tickets online rather than wait in line when we arrive.

3. Even though it was raining, the coach made us do five laps.

4. I'm going over to Aria's house as soon as I finish practising violin.

5. The plane finally landed after it had circled the airport for twenty minutes.

6. Although it is summer, we are not going to the cottage on Lake of the Woods this year.

B. **Write a sentence that has an independent clause and a subordinate clause, using the conjunction provided. Place the subordinate clause either before or after the independent clause.**

1. as long as

_____

_____

2. whenever

_____

_____

_____

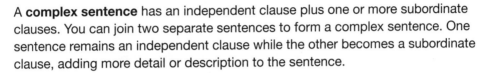

COMBINE SENTENCES: COMPLEX SENTENCES

A **complex sentence** has an independent clause plus one or more subordinate clauses. You can join two separate sentences to form a complex sentence. One sentence remains an independent clause while the other becomes a subordinate clause, adding more detail or description to the sentence.

You can join a subordinate clause to an independent clause with a conjunction, such as *after*, *before*, *because*, *unless*, *if*, *when*, *although*, or *as soon as*, or with a relative pronoun, such as *who*, *which*, or *that*.

> For example: Ella sprained her ankle at soccer practice. She had to get crutches.
> *Because* she sprained her ankle at soccer practice, Ella had to get crutches. (conjunction *because*)
> Ella, *who* sprained her ankle at soccer practice, had to get crutches. (relative pronoun *who*)

If you place the subordinate clause before the independent clause, always follow the subordinate clause with a comma, as in the second example. When a subordinate clause begins with a relative pronoun, set it apart with commas, as in the third example, unless it is needed to identify the subject.

A. Combine the two independent clauses to make a complex sentence. Use a conjunction or a relative pronoun from the list below.

as soon as   which   when

1. My family visited the National Art Gallery in Ottawa. I was seven.

_____

2. School was over. Tamar raced home.

_____

3. Our science project is due on Monday. It is on sustainable development.

_____

B. Rewrite each sentence as a complex sentence by adding a subordinate clause.

1. I finished my speech.

_____

2. We arrived at the stadium early.

_____

C. Write two complex sentences about active living. For one sentence, use a conjunction to join the subordinate clause to an independent clause. For the other sentence, use a relative pronoun.

1. _____

_____

2. _____

_____

D. Imagine you could travel back in time. Write three paragraphs about a time period you would like to visit and explain why. Experiment with writing complex sentences using conjunctions and relative pronouns. Include at least three complex sentences.

_____

_____

_____

_____

_____

_____

_____

_____

_____

_____

_____

_____

_____

_____

_____

_____

_____

_____

_____

_____

RECOGNIZE CLAUSES: ADJECTIVE CLAUSES

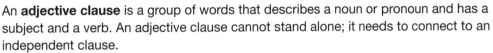

An **adjective clause** is a group of words that describes a noun or pronoun and has a subject and a verb. An adjective clause cannot stand alone; it needs to connect to an independent clause.

For example: The man *who lives next door* likes gardening.

In the example, *who lives next door* is the adjective clause. It describes a noun, *man*, and it cannot stand on its own. Adjective clauses can begin with words such as *who, whom, whose, that, which, when, where,* or *why*.

Some adjective clauses are essential, and some are nonessential. Essential clauses identify the noun or pronoun, and are needed for the sentence to make sense. Nonessential clauses simply add more information about the noun. If you removed a nonessential clause, the meaning of the sentence would not change. Nonessential clauses are always set apart with commas, while essential clauses are not.

For example: The man *who lives next door* likes gardening. (essential)
Mr. Howard, *who lives next door,* likes gardening. (nonessential)

In the first example, *who lives next door* is an essential clause because it is needed to identify which man is being discussed. In the second example, *who lives next door* is a nonessential clause because the man is identified as Mr. Howard.

A. **Underline the adjective clause in each sentence. Then, decide if the clause is essential or nonessential. Write either *E* for essential clause or *N* for nonessential clause on the line beside each sentence.**

1. Last weekend, when my grandparents visited, we went to the museum. _____

2. I want the cake that has chocolate icing and vanilla filling. _____

3. At choir practice, Gloria met another girl who likes mystery novels. _____

4. The old library building, which is next to the fire station, is being torn down. _____

B. **Write two sentences about a trip you've taken or would like to take. Use an adjective clause in each sentence.**

1. _____

_____

2. _____

_____

C. **Underline the adjective clause in each sentence from Exercise B. Then, decide whether each clause is essential or nonessential.**

RECOGNIZE CLAUSES: ADVERB CLAUSES

An **adverb clause** is a group of words, including a subject and a verb, that modifies a verb, an adjective, or another adverb.

An adverb clause usually answers the question *where?* (place), *when?* (time), *why?* (reason), or *how?* (under what condition). It always begins with a conjunction, such as *after, before, when, while, since, where, as, if, so, unless, because,* or *although.*

For example: She left her keys *where she knew she would find them.* (place)
Mareike arrived *before the show started.* (time)
I took a deep breath *because I was nervous.* (reason)
David kept dancing *although his feet hurt.* (condition)

You can place an adverb clause at the beginning or end of a sentence. If you place it at the beginning, the adverb clause should be followed with a comma.
For example: *While the song was playing,* David kept dancing.

A. Underline the adverb clause in each sentence. Then, identify what question it answers (*where? when? why?* or *how?*).

1. The volleyball players were upset because they didn't make it to the finals. _____

2. When I got to the store, I realized I had forgotten my wallet. _____

3. I'll get an A in science class unless I fail the exam. _____

4. Jackson waited where his mom had told him to wait. _____

5. Before I printed my essay, I read through it one more time. _____

6. Paul put on two pairs of socks so his feet would not get cold. _____

B. Write a paragraph about preparing for an important event in your life. Include at least two sentences with adverb clauses. Underline each adverb clause.

___ _____

___ _____

_____

_____

_____

C. Look through some articles. Find two sentences with adverb clauses. Identify whether the adverb clause answers a question about the place, time, reason, or condition of the action.

EDIT SENTENCES: SENTENCE FRAGMENTS

A **sentence fragment** is a group of words that is punctuated like a sentence but is not complete. One kind of sentence fragment is missing a subject or a verb.

For example: Went outside to get the mail. (missing subject)

Mosquitoes all over the ceiling. (missing verb)

To fix this type of sentence fragment, add the missing subject or verb.

Another type of sentence fragment is a participle phrase fragment. A participle phrase begins with either a present participle verb, which ends in –ing (*working, hiding*), or a past participle verb, which often ends in –ed or –en (*worked, hidden*). A participle phrase cannot stand on its own because it does not express a complete thought.

For example: Working on her drum solo.

Hidden under the seat.

To fix a participle phrase fragment, add the noun or pronoun that the phrase is modifying, or add an independent clause.

For example: Working on her drum solo, *Alma didn't hear the doorbell*.

(independent clause added)

The notebook was hidden under the seat.

(noun + linking verb added)

A. **Read each group of words and decide if it is a sentence or a sentence fragment. Write *S* for sentence or *SF* for sentence fragment on the line.**

1. Moving slowly across the field. _____

2. Hassan looked up in surprise. _____

3. An expert in health and well-being. _____

4. Followed by a presentation on renewable energy. _____

B. **Correct the following sentence fragments:**

1. Tripping over his shoelaces and falling flat on his face.

_____

_____

2. Written on a piece of scrap paper.

_____

_____

C. **In your own words, write a definition for *sentence fragment*. How can you tell if a group of words is a complete sentence or a sentence fragment?**

EDIT SENTENCES: COMMA SPLICES

A **comma splice** occurs when a comma is used to connect two independent clauses. This is an incorrect use of a comma.

> For example: There were no empty seats, we stood at the back. ✗

There are three different ways to fix comma splices:

1. Make two separate sentences.
   > For example: There were no empty seats. We stood at the back. ✓

2. Add a coordinating conjunction (*and, but, or, so*) or a subordinating conjunction (*after, although, because, before, since, unless, whenever, wherever*).
   > For example: There were no empty seats, *so* we stood at the back. ✓
   > *Because* there were no empty seats, we stood at the back. ✓

3. Replace the comma with a semicolon.
   > For example: There were no empty seats; we stood at the back. ✓

A. Read each sentence. Write an *X* if the sentence has a comma splice or a check mark (✓) if the sentence is correct.

1. After the show, we all went out for pizza. _____

2. I went to the doctor, she said I was healthy. _____

3. The diving board was high, and I was scared to look down. _____

4. Unless we put up posters for the missing cat, nobody will help. _____

B. Fix the comma splice in each sentence.

1. The kitchen is a mess, we have to clean up before Mom gets home.

   _____

   _____

2. Driving to school is faster, riding a bike is better for your health and the environment.

   _____

   _____

3. I edited my essay, it had a few spelling mistakes.

   _____

   _____

C. Review the sentences you wrote for Exercise B and correct any errors. Then rewrite the sentences, finding a second way to fix each comma splice.

SECTION REVIEW

A. For each sentence, add correct end punctuation on the short line. Then, identify each sentence type by writing "Declarative," "Imperative," "Interrogative," or "Exclamatory" on the long line.

1. Find out why Noa wasn't at school today___ _____

2. What an amazing show___ _____

3. Are you free to study after class today___ _____

4. The track and field practice is cancelled today___ _____

B. Are the following sentences compound sentences? Circle either *Yes* or *No*.

1. Ask me again tomorrow; I will have made up my mind by then.　　Yes　　No

2. The student council election is next week, but I don't think I will　　Yes　　No

   get elected.

3. My favourite dessert is chocolate cake and ice cream.　　Yes　　No

C. Expand each sentence by adding at least one adjective or adjective phrase and one adverb or adverb phrase.

1. My sister studied.

   _____

   _____

2. The team celebrated.

   _____

   _____

D. Choose the best way to correct each run-on sentence. Add a comma and a conjunction, break it into two sentences, or add a semicolon.

1. The test was hard I studied all night.

   _____

2. Jay won the race he hurt his ankle.

   _____

E. Underline the simple subject and circle the simple predicate in each sentence.

1. The red car parked across the street has three flat tires.

2. The public buses in our neighbourhood have been arriving at least ten minutes late.

F. Underline the compound subject or compound predicate in each sentence. Then, write *CS* for compound subject or *CP* for compound predicate.

1. The two friends will go to a movie or swim in the pool. _____

2. Carmina's purse and shoes got soaked in the thunderstorm. _____

3. The tomatoes and peppers are ready to be picked. _____

4. We ran out of the water and grabbed our towels. _____

G. Underline the direct object and circle the indirect object in each sentence.

1. We made name tags for all of the guests at the party.

2. Nolan emailed instructions to Brent for downloading the game.

3. The professor gave a long lecture to the students.

4. My sister gave me a look that surprised me.

H. Write four sentences. Each should have an independent clause and a subordinate clause, and should use one of the conjunctions provided. Remember to use a comma after the subordinate clause if it comes before the independent clause.

1. (before) _____

_____

2. (rather than) _____

_____

3. (as long as) _____

_____

4. (whenever) _____

_____

I. Underline the adjective clause in each sentence. Write *E* if the clause is essential or *N* if the clause is nonessential.

1. My sister's friend who plays violin is in the recital next Friday. _____

2. Last February, when it was really cold out, I got frostbite on my ears. _____

3. We got a dog that has shaggy hair and brown and white spots. _____

J. Correct the following sentence fragments and comma-splice errors.

1. Given to the top student in the class. _____

_____

2. Carly went first, I followed close behind her. _____

_____

3. Finishing my essay on human rights in Canada. _____

_____

K. **Write two paragraphs about the benefit of having a positive attitude during a difficult time. Use a variety of short, medium, and long sentences. Choose three of your sentences; underline the complete subject and circle the complete predicate in each one.**

L. Write two paragraphs about a performer, athlete, or politician you admire and explain your reasons for choosing them. Include at least two complex sentences. Underline each complex sentence.

KNOW CAPITALIZATION AND PUNCTUATION

There are many rules in every language, from how to spell a word to how to end a sentence. Most of the rules are ones you should make a habit of following—otherwise, your message will be difficult to understand, and people might not take your writing seriously.

Some of the rules, such as when to use a comma, have a little more flexibility. But, like learning a new game, you need to know the rules before you can begin playing.

In this section, you will get to know these rules so that you can guide readers through your writing just the way you want to.

"When speaking aloud, you punctuate constantly—with body language. Your listener hears commas, dashes, question marks, exclamation points, and quotation marks as you shout, whisper, pause, wave your arms, roll your eyes, and wrinkle your brow."

— Russel Baker

USE CAPITALS: A VARIETY OF CAPITALIZATION

We use **capitals** for the following kinds of words:
- the first word in a sentence
- the first word and other important words in a heading, subheading, or title of a song, poem, book, or story
- days of the week, months of the year, holidays and special days
- important and specific places, events, historical periods, and documents
- the planets and other specific objects in the universe
- important words in the names of awards (such as *Most Valuable Player*)
- adjectives formed from proper nouns (such as *French* or *Shakespearean*)
- proper nouns (such as the names of people, organizations, and schools)
- abbreviations of days and months, forms of address, places, and geographical features

We also capitalize a person's title (or the abbreviations of the title), but only when it is followed by the person's name.

For example: We waited for *Admiral* <u>Boyle</u> to give the command.
We waited for the *admiral* to give the command.

A. **Read each phrase and decide if it is capitalized correctly. Write "Yes" or "No" on the line after the phrase. If you write "No," underline the words that have errors.**

1. the most beautiful garden Award _____

2. the 78-year-old Argentinian pope _____

3. *The History of orchids* _____

4. Callisto, a moon of Jupiter _____

B. **Rewrite this journal entry, adding capitals wherever necessary.**

sept. 4th: Today I read a poem that reminded me of greece. "easter on the mediterranean sea" made me think of our outing with captain markos. what a beautiful night sky we saw I have never seen so many constellations: leo, virgo, and ursa minor were just a few.

_____

_____

_____

_____

C. **Review the paragraph you rewrote for Exercise B. Did you capitalize the correct words? Write down each word you capitalized, and beside each word, write the kind of word it is. See the box at the top of the page for help.**

KNOW LATIN SHORT FORMS: ABBREVIATIONS

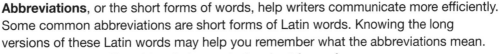

Abbreviations, or the short forms of words, help writers communicate more efficiently. Some common abbreviations are short forms of Latin words. Knowing the long versions of these Latin words may help you remember what the abbreviations mean.

For example: The abbreviation *vs.* is the short form of *versus,* which is Latin for "against."

The abbreviation *i.e.* is the short form of *id est*, which is Latin for "that is."

A. **Fill in the right-hand column by writing the correct abbreviation of each Latin phrase. Choose from the following abbreviations:**

PS   c.   CV   e.g.   etc.   re   a.m.   vs.

Latin Phrase	English Translation	Abbreviation
et cetera	and the rest / and so on	
post scriptum	after what has been written	
curriculum vitae	course of life	
versus	against	
ante meridiem	before midday	
exempli gratia	for example	
circa	around / approximately	
re	with reference to	

B. **Rewrite each sentence, replacing the underlined phrase with a Latin-based abbreviation.**

1. We can all improve in many areas: fitness, nutrition, stress relief, <u>and so on.</u>

_____

2. First, set a measurable goal, <u>for example,</u> "I will run three times a week."

_____

3. Then, make sure you measure your progress, <u>that is,</u> record your actions.

_____

C. **Look up the following abbreviations in a dictionary: *et al., p.m., PhD.* Write down the Latin and English meanings of each abbreviation. Use each abbreviation in a sentence.**

SHORTEN BUSINESS WORDS: ABBREVIATIONS

Abbreviations, or the short forms of words, help writers communicate more quickly. Abbreviations can also make writing easier to read because they replace long and/or difficult words.

People in the business world, for example, use abbreviations to communicate quickly and informally through emails or texts. There are many business abbreviations with which you should be familiar.

For example: The abbreviation *Inc.* at the end of a business name, like *Digging Wells For Hope, Inc.,* indicates that this company is *incorporated*. That means it is legally a company.

A group's name could end instead with *Assn.* or *Org.,* meaning the group is an *association* or an *organization*. Both these words refer to groups that are formed of people who share a goal or set of interests.

A. Answer each question by choosing the correct meaning for the underlined abbreviation. Circle your answers.

1. What kind of business is Lakeside Condominium <u>Corp</u>.?

    a) a federation   **b)** a division   **c)** a corporation

2. Lindsay works in the Music <u>Dept</u>. Which word describes where she works?

    a) Division   **b)** Department   **c)** Development

B. Rewrite the conversation. Replace each underlined phrase with one of the following abbreviations. Note that you will need to choose four of the six abbreviations listed below:

dept.   HQ   mfg.   ETA   ASAP   mgmt.

"Mr. Longo, what's your <u>estimated time of arrival</u> at <u>headquarters</u>?"

_____

"Sandy, I'm leaving our <u>manufacturing</u> <u>department</u> now, so I won't be long."

_____

C. Rewrite this message, using the long form of each underlined abbreviation.

Our <u>org.</u> has won an award! Tell all <u>dept.</u> managers <u>ASAP</u>!

_____

D. Write your own message using abbreviations. Circle the abbreviations.

SEPARATE ADJECTIVES: COMMAS

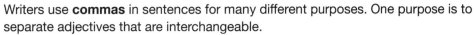

Writers use **commas** in sentences for many different purposes. One purpose is to separate adjectives that are interchangeable.

> For example: He made a *spicy, beefy* stew. = He made a *beefy, spicy* stew.

In the example, *spicy* and *beefy* are adjectives that describe the stew. The order in which they are listed does not matter; they are interchangeable. Therefore, you use a comma between them.

If two adjectives are *not* interchangeable, however, you *do not* use a comma to separate them.

> For example: He made a *spicy vegetable* stew.

In the example, *spicy* and *vegetable* are the adjectives that describe the stew. But you would not say "He made a *vegetable spicy* stew." That means the two adjectives are *not* interchangeable, so you *do not* use a comma between them.

A. **In each phrase, decide whether the two adjectives are interchangeable. Write "Yes" or "No" on the line after each phrase. If you write "Yes," add a comma between the adjectives.**

1. a brown male dog   _____   **4.** a hungry tired team   _____

2. a kind police officer   _____   **5.** a filling healthy meal   _____

3. dependable public transit   _____   **6.** fake cheap merchandise   _____

B. **Complete each sentence with the two adjectives provided. Add a comma between them if necessary.**

1. Out of the shadows came a _____ man. (giant / mechanical)

2. In a _____ voice, Caitlin said, "Stop!" (confident / strong)

C. **For each noun and pair of adjectives provided, write a sentence. Include a comma between the adjectives if necessary.**

1. syrup: maple / delicious

_____

2. friend: intelligent / humourous

_____

3. island: desert / tropical

_____

D. **Write a few paragraphs describing your favourite place or your favourite memory. Use as many pairs of adjectives as you can. Use commas if necessary.**

PUNCTUATE DIALOGUE: QUOTATION MARKS

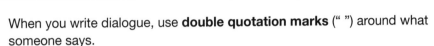

When you write dialogue, use **double quotation marks** (" ") around what someone says.

For example: Jay asked, "What story are you reading?"

Notice that end punctuation goes *before* the last double quotation mark.

Use **single quotation marks** (' ') around the title of a story, poem, or song *within* someone's speech.

For example: Kylie said, "I'm reading 'To Build a Fire.' It's by Jack London."

Here again, the first period goes *before* the last single quotation mark, and the last period goes *before* the last double quotation mark.

Also use single quotation marks inside double quotation marks if the speaker quotes a person or a text.

For example: She continued, "The story starts like this: 'Day had broken cold and grey …'"

Notice again that the punctuation appears *before* the last single quotation mark, which appears *before* the last double quotation mark.

A. **Complete each sentence by filling in the missing punctuation. Use a single quotation mark, a double quotation mark, or both.**

1. The carpenter said, " _____ Do it right the first time' is my motto."

2. The carpenter said, "My motto, 'Do it right the first time,' is on my business card._____

3. The carpenter said, "My motto is 'Do it right the first time._____

B. **The following sentences are missing all of their quotation marks. Add the correct marks in the correct places.**

1. Jay said, I like the story Brown Wolf better than To Build a Fire.

2. Marcus said, I think both stories are pretty sad, don't you?

3. Jay answered, Yes, but I like that the writer describes dogs so accurately.

C. **Write three lines of dialogue in which each line includes the poem title "The Raven." Make one line of dialogue a question, one a statement, and one an exclamation. Use the starters below.**

Kiara asked, _____

Cedric answered, _____

Kiara exclaimed, _____

D. Write a conversation among three people discussing a song. Use single and double quotation marks correctly.

_____

_____

_____

_____

_____

_____

_____

_____

_____

_____

_____

_____

_____

_____

_____

_____

_____

_____

_____

_____

_____

_____

_____

_____

SHOW POSSESSION: APOSTROPHES

When you want to show possession or ownership, follow these rules for **apostrophes** ('):

For singular nouns (including those ending in s), add apostrophe + s.
　For example:　the *witness's* testimony (the testimony of one witness)

For plural nouns ending in s, add only an apostrophe.
　For example:　the *binoculars'* lenses (the lenses of several binoculars)

For plural nouns that do not end in s, add apostrophe + s.
　For example:　your *teeth's* condition (the condition of several teeth)

For two or more nouns that possess something together, make only the last noun possessive.
　For example:　Counsellor Nitesh and *Counsellor Dufoix's* opinions are well respected. (The opinions of *both* counsellors.)

For two or more nouns that each possesses something separately, make each noun possessive.
　For example:　*Counsellor Nitesh's* and *Counsellor Dufoix's* opinions are well respected. (Some opinions belong to Counsellor Nitesh, and some opinions belong to Counsellor Dufoix. Each counsellor has separate opinions.)

A. In each sentence, make the appropriate nouns possessive. Either write ' or 's on the line or leave the line blank.

1. Jules and Nuala wrote a blog together. It was Jules＿＿＿ and Nuala＿＿＿ blog.

2. Each writer made up a fake profile. They were Jules＿＿＿ and Nuala＿＿＿ profiles.

3. Many classmates left comments on the blog. They were the classmates＿＿＿ comments.

B. In each sentence, find the noun that is missing an apostrophe to show possession. Write the noun, with the apostrophe added, on the line after the sentence.

1. One of Averys talents is writing songs. ＿＿＿＿＿＿＿＿＿＿

2. Her songs lyrics are often very personal. ＿＿＿＿＿＿＿＿＿＿

3. She also writes childrens songs, which her little brothers love. ＿＿＿＿＿＿＿＿＿＿

4. Her brothers favourite song is "What My Nose Knows." ＿＿＿＿＿＿＿＿＿＿

5. At her familys annual reunion, Avery played several new songs. ＿＿＿＿＿＿＿＿＿＿

C. Write two sentences about something that belongs to people in your school. In each sentence, use the possessive forms for at least two different types of nouns mentioned in this lesson.

USE TRANSITION WORDS: SEMICOLONS

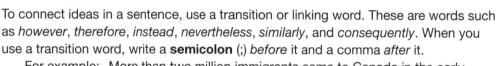

To connect ideas in a sentence, use a transition or linking word. These are words such as *however*, *therefore*, *instead*, *nevertheless*, *similarly*, and *consequently*. When you use a transition word, write a **semicolon** (;) *before* it and a comma *after* it.

For example: More than two million immigrants came to Canada in the early 1900s. (idea one)
The population's diversity increased significantly. (idea two)
More than two million immigrants came to Canada in the early 1900s; *consequently*, the population's diversity increased significantly.

Notice that the transition word after the semicolon does not begin with a capital letter. Also note that the group of words on either side of the semicolon is an independent clause. This means each group of words can stand on its own as a sentence.

A. In each sentence, underline the two independent clauses. Then, circle the transition word.

1. In the early 1900s, much of Canada remained unsettled; nevertheless, people came for the opportunities the country offered.

2. Cities were growing quickly because of the wave of newcomers; therefore, construction jobs were plentiful.

B. In each sentence, underline the transition word. Then, write a semicolon before the transition word, between the two independent clauses.

1. The Canadian government wanted immigrants to settle the Prairies however, it did not treat all newcomers equally.

2. People from the same region often had a lot in common consequently, they tended to settle close to one another.

C. Join the two independent clauses to form one sentence. Write each sentence on a line, using a semicolon and the appropriate transition word between the two clauses.

Clause 1: Many immigrants came to Canada planning to make money and return home.

Clause 2: They remained in the country and became part of its identity.

_____

_____

_____

_____

D. Write two paragraphs comparing your favourite food to your least favourite food. Include at least three sentences that use semicolons and transition words to link ideas.

_____

_____

_____

_____

_____

_____

_____

_____

_____

_____

_____

_____

_____

_____

_____

_____

_____

_____

_____

_____

_____

_____

_____

_____

_____

E. Reread some of your writing, looking for short, choppy sentences. Find at least two places where you could combine two related sentences into one, using a semicolon and a transition word. Rewrite the sentences. Think about how the flow of your writing changes.

INTRODUCE A LIST: COLONS

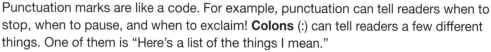

Punctuation marks are like a code. For example, punctuation can tell readers when to stop, when to pause, and when to exclaim! **Colons** (:) can tell readers a few different things. One of them is "Here's a list of the things I mean."

For example: We learned about online risk: cyberbullying, phishing scams, and inappropriate images.

In the example sentence, the colon indicates, "Here's a list of some of the situations I mean." When you use a colon this way, make sure that a complete sentence comes *before* the colon and the list. Do not use a colon after a preposition or a verb.

For example: We learned how to: handle cyberbullying, avoid phishing scams, and deal with inappropriate images. ✗ (incorrect use after a preposition)

We learned how to handle: cyberbullying, phishing scams, and inappropriate images. ✗ (incorrect use after a verb)

A. Each sentence is missing a colon. Add the colon where it is needed. Make sure it follows a complete sentence.

1. Coach Henley gave us some tips for how to spend the night before the big game don't practise in case you hurt yourself, eat a healthy dinner, and get a good sleep.

2. I was a bit nervous before the game because I knew several people in the audience my three cousins, my aunt, and my two best friends.

3. We had a great time yesterday we ate pizza, had ice cream, and went to the movies.

4. Next year I have three goals to become a better hitter, to learn how to play shortstop, and to steal a base.

B. Each sentence uses a colon incorrectly. Choose one of the following reasons to explain why the colon is incorrect:

a) It appears after a preposition.   **b)** It appears after a verb.

c) It appears after an incomplete sentence.

1. Information you shouldn't share online: your address, your phone number, and your passwords. ____

2. Volunteering is important for: gaining experience, meeting people, and learning new things. ____

3. A food nutrition label includes: serving size, number of calories, and fat content. ____

4. Good team members: cooperate, listen, encourage one another, and work toward the same goal. ____

C. Write a sentence that includes a list of items. Experiment with placing the colon in different spots in the sentence.

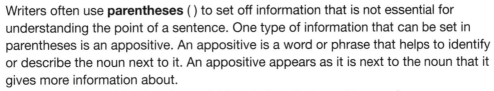

ADD APPOSITIVES: PARENTHESES

Writers often use **parentheses** ( ) to set off information that is not essential for understanding the point of a sentence. One type of information that can be set in parentheses is an appositive. An appositive is a word or phrase that helps to identify or describe the noun next to it. An appositive appears as it is next to the noun that it gives more information about.

For example: Mr. Khan (our neighbour) shovelled our driveway for us.

In the example, *our neighbour* is an appositive that helps to identify Mr. Khan. Note that appositives can also be set off using commas.

For example: Mr. Khan, our neighbour, shovelled our driveway for us.

If you are not sure whether a word or phrase is an appositive in your sentence, try removing it. If the point of the sentence is still clear, you can set the word or phrase in parentheses.

Remember that parentheses come in pairs: one parenthesis comes before the less important information and one comes after it.

A. In each sentence, draw the missing parentheses around the appositive.

1. Our farmers' market the largest in the region runs on Saturdays and Wednesdays.

2. We buy honey usually organic from a local beekeeping operation.

3. Once we even got some fiddleheads or young ferns because they looked so strange!

B. Read each sentence and the appositive underneath it. Rewrite the sentence, adding the appositive after the noun. Be sure to use parentheses around the appositive.

1. Yuko and his family have just relocated to the city of Victoria.

Appositive: on Vancouver Island

_____

_____

2. Yuko was thrilled to discover that the city has many bike lanes.

Appositive: an avid cyclist

_____

_____

C. Write a paragraph about your most important possession. Use appositives in parentheses to give information.

GUIDE READERS: A VARIETY OF PUNCTUATION

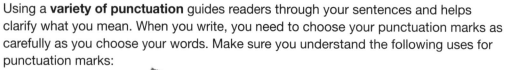

Using a **variety of punctuation** guides readers through your sentences and helps clarify what you mean. When you write, you need to choose your punctuation marks as carefully as you choose your words. Make sure you understand the following uses for punctuation marks:

- commas to separate adjectives
- double quotation marks around dialogue
- single quotation marks around quotes *within* dialogue
- apostrophes to show possession or ownership
- semicolons between two independent clauses
- colons to introduce lists
- parentheses to set off appositives

A. Rewrite each of the following phrases on the line, adding the adjective provided. Use a comma in the correct place.

1. a fresh salad (add *healthy*): _____

2. wide bike routes (add *safe*): _____

3. windy grasslands (add *warm*): _____ _____

B. In each sentence, find the noun that is missing an apostrophe to show possession. Write the noun, with the apostrophe added.

1. The artists paintings reflected the peace they found in nature. _____ ___

2. This photographers website shows more of her photos. _____

3. My aunt performs as a clown at childrens parties. _____

C. Each sentence has two parts. Decide whether a semicolon or a colon is the best choice to separate each part. Add the correct mark in the appropriate place.

1. People in many parts of the world do not have access to clean water however, organizations such as Water for People are working for change.

2. Communities can do many things to become more sustainable start recycling programs, encourage roof gardens, and use renewable energy sources.

D. Rewrite the following sentence, adding the suggested appositive after the noun. Use parentheses around the appositive.

War Child is dedicated to improving the lives of children.

Appositive: founded in 1999

_____

E. Write a conversation between two friends about their favourite songs. Be sure to use double and single quotation marks correctly.

_____

_____

_____

_____

_____

_____

_____

_____

_____

_____

_____

_____

_____

_____

_____

_____

_____

_____

_____

_____

_____

_____

_____

F. Write an example sentence for each type of punctuation listed in the box at the beginning of this lesson. Make sure your examples are original and creative.

SECTION REVIEW

A. In each sentence, underline the letter that should be capitalized.

1. conservation officer singh has been a parks canada employee since 2011.

2. the officer is a tour guide at fort steele in british columbia.

3. the fort is close to wild horse creek, where gold was found in the 1800s.

4. officer singh wrote a book called *the rebirth of fort steele: embracing our heritage.*

5. officer singh's book won the bc history award in sept. 2017.

B. For each abbreviation, choose the correct meaning.

1. etc. = and so on / that is

2. e.g. = with reference to / for example

3. i.e. = that is / approximately

4. dept. = development / department

5. mgmt. = manufacturing / management

6. ASAP = association / as soon as possible

C. Rewrite each sentence, adding any commas that are missing in between adjectives.

1. Merida asked the young friendly waiter for a toasted cheese sandwich.

   _____

2. The energetic spotless cook delivered the fresh delicious food personally.

   _____

D. Rewrite the dialogue below, adding single and double quotation marks where they are missing.

Darla said, I need a slogan for my election campaign.

Here's one: Vote for Darla—she's darling! offered Chris.

That's terrible! exclaimed Darla. Daring Darla can do the job!

Chris commented, That sounds much better.

_____

_____

_____

_____

_____

_____

E. Underline the possessive that correctly completes each item.

1 Fernie is famous for its weekend (farmers' / farmers's) market.

2. The (townspeoples' / townspeople's) favourite stall is the one with the cheese samples.

3. The cheddar (cheese's / cheeses) claim to fame is its unusual colour.

4. The Thomson twins run a stall together at the market. It's called (Paula's and Patrick's / Paula and Patrick's) Produce.

5. The (twins's / twins') younger sister helps them in the stall.

F. Join each pair of independent clauses to form one sentence, using the transition word provided. Be sure to use semicolons and commas correctly.

1. The invention of the telescope has increased our knowledge of the universe. Microscope technology has allowed us to learn more about our own bodies.

(similarly) _____

_____

2. Our understanding of cells has led to several breakthroughs in medicine. It has also led to the creation of products such as pesticides.

(however)_____

_____

G. Decide whether each sentence uses a colon correctly. Write either "Yes" or "No", and then write a brief explanation of your answer.

1. The Indigenous peoples of Canada include three groups: Métis, First Nations, and Inuit. _____

_____

2. The majority of Francophones in Canada live in: Quebec, Ontario, or New Brunswick. _____

_____

H. Rewrite the paragraph, adding parentheses around the appositives.

We met our guide Santini at Café Nova, a restaurant in the town square. From there, we travelled by *boita* a type of boat to Castle Luffgard. There, we met an *asistente* an attendant of the emperor, who escorted us into the throne room. Roxelana the empress greeted us warmly and offered us a cup of Dragon Well, which is a rare green tea.

_____

_____

_____

_____

_____

_____

I. **Write two paragraphs explaining the major and minor characters in a book or movie. Mention the names of the characters and use appositives in parentheses to help identify or describe them. Use colons to introduce any lists.**

_____

_____

_____

_____

_____

_____

_____

_____

_____

_____

_____

_____

_____

_____

_____

_____

_____

_____

_____

_____

_____

_____

_____

_____

_____

_____

_____

_____

J. Write a short dialogue between two friends discussing their favourite artists (visual or musical) and explaining some of the artists' works. Be sure to form possessives correctly and to use single and double quotation marks correctly.

_____

_____

_____

_____

_____

_____

_____

_____

_____

_____

_____

_____

_____

_____

_____

_____

_____

_____

_____

_____

_____

_____

_____

_____

_____

_____

_____

GRASP GRAMMAR AND USAGE

Grammar is the underlying framework of how language works. You might not know all the rules by name, but you use them whenever you write or speak.

Without grammar, writing would just be a mixed-up jumble of words. Grammar tells us what should come first in a sentence, what should come next, and how these two things are related. Without the right grammar, your writing will sound wrong, even if you're not sure why.

In this section, you will learn how paying attention to grammar can improve your writing.

"We are not nouns; we are verbs. I am not a thing—an actor, a writer. I am a person who does things—I write, I act, and I never know what I'm going to do next. I think you can be imprisoned if you think of yourself as a noun."

— Stephen Fry

NAME THE PERSON, PLACE, THING, OR IDEA: NOUNS

A **noun** is a word that names a person, place, thing, idea, or feeling.

A common noun names a general person, place, thing, idea, or feeling.
> For example: musician (person), arena (place), monument (thing), courage (idea), pride (feeling)

A proper noun names a specific person, place, or thing.
> For example: Ms. Prasad (person), Yukon (place), Health Canada (thing)

A collective noun names a group of people or things.
> For example: council, Senate, flock

A compound noun is formed by combining two or more words. A compound noun can be one word, two words, or hyphenated; use a dictionary to be sure.
> For example: groundwater, water bottle, vice-president

A. **Underline the nouns in each sentence.**

1. To raise money for our foster child, our school held an auction of artwork created by students.

2. WE Charity is an organization that began in Canada and empowers youth around the world.

3. Last summer, Aunt Monique volunteered as a house-builder for a local charity.

4. For the Brookton Science Fair, Jaya and Wes created a simple pump for use in communities that lack clean water.

5. Our class uses various media to stay aware of international issues and events.

6. People in our former village lost their homes in the recent earthquake.

B. **Identify each noun as a common noun (COM), proper noun (PR), or collective noun (COL).**

1. assistant _____	**4.** officer _____	**7.** committee _____
2. beach _____	**5.** software _____	**8.** jury _____
3. Saskatoon _____	**6.** Dr. Lau _____	**9.** Order of Canada _____

C. **Write a compound noun for each definition. Use a dictionary to check if the noun is one word, two words, or hyphenated.**

1. an outdoor movie theatre _____

2. a place to mail letters and parcels _____

3. the programs for a computer _____

4. a sport with three "outs" _____

5. where you wash your clothes _____

D. Write one or more paragraphs about a charitable organization that you would be interested in volunteering for. Describe what the organization does and why it appeals to you. Use a variety of nouns in your writing, including proper nouns, collective nouns, and compound nouns.

_____

_____

_____

_____

_____

_____

_____

_____

_____

_____

_____

_____

_____

_____

_____

_____

_____

_____

_____

_____

_____

_____

_____

E. Write down five book titles. For each title, underline the nouns and identify them as common, collective, or proper.

SHOW OWNERSHIP: SINGULAR POSSESSIVE NOUNS

Possessive nouns are a concise way of showing ownership. For example, instead of writing "the safety of the student," you can write "the student's safety."

A **singular possessive noun** shows that one person, place, thing, or idea owns or has something. To make a singular noun possessive, you simply add an apostrophe (') followed by the letter *s*.

For example: the *writer's* idea; *Regina's* city hall; the *monkey's* tail; *culture's* role

If a singular noun already ends in *s*, you still just add an apostrophe plus *s* to make the possessive.

For example: the *witness's* statement; *Trois-Rivières's* weather; the *glass's* rim

A. Rewrite each phrase using a singular possessive noun.

1. marriage of the duchess _____

2. fillings of the sandwich _____

3. software of the computer _____

4. habitat of the fox _____

B. Complete each sentence by writing the correct possessive version of the noun in parentheses.

1. Several factors affect our _____ sustainability. (community)

2. The _____ speech at the opening of the reserve's two new businesses was inspiring to everyone in the community. (chief)

3. After hearing _____ report on urbanization, we discussed our own experiences living in the city. (Travis)

4. I often wonder about what our _____ landscape will look like in the future. (area)

5. With no cellphone and my _____ lens shattered, I was anxious about getting lost. (compass)

C. Write a sentence using the singular possessive form of the noun *business*.

_____

_____

D. Select five objects that you see in your home and write a brief sentence describing each one. Use a singular possessive noun in each sentence. Thinks about the rules for forming the possessive form of singular nouns.

SHOW OWNERSHIP: PLURAL POSSESSIVE NOUNS

Possessive nouns are a concise way of showing ownership. For example, instead of writing "the luggage of the passengers," you can write "the passengers' luggage."

Most plural nouns end in *s*. To form a **plural possessive noun** from a noun ending in *s*, you just add an apostrophe (') after the final *s*.

For example: the *referees'* whistles (the whistles belong to the referees)
the *wolves'* behaviour (the behaviour belongs to the wolves)
the *bullies'* apologies (the apologies belong to the bullies)
the *groups'* effort (the effort belongs to the groups)

Possessive nouns always have an apostrophe. If you add an apostrophe to a noun, make sure you are doing so to show possession. Plural nouns that are not possessive do not need an apostrophe.

A. **Decide if the underlined possessive noun is singular or plural. Write *S* for singular or *P* for plural.**

1. The old <u>piano's</u> keys were brittle and discoloured. ____

2. The <u>graphs'</u> climate data showed some inconsistencies. ____

3. The <u>fortresses'</u> massive doors were made of iron. ____

4. The soccer <u>teams'</u> uniforms each had a different logo. ____

B. **Write a sentence using the possessive form of each plural noun.**

1. foxes _____

2. studios _____

3. tomatoes _____

C. **Change the underlined part of each sentence to include a plural possessive noun. Rewrite the sentence, with the new wording.**

1. <u>The prey of the seagulls</u> includes fish, worms, insects, and reptiles.

_____

2. <u>The mountains of these areas</u> are volcanic.

_____

D. **Find three examples of plural possessive nouns in a recent newspaper article or headline. Rewrite each plural possessive noun as a phrase, as in, "the _____ belonging to the _____."**

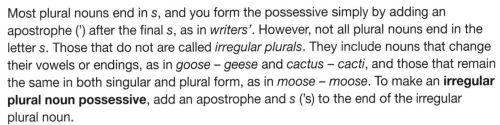

MAKE IRREGULAR PLURAL NOUNS POSSESSIVE

Most plural nouns end in *s*, and you form the possessive simply by adding an apostrophe (') after the final *s*, as in *writers'*. However, not all plural nouns end in the letter *s*. Those that do not are called *irregular plurals*. They include nouns that change their vowels or endings, as in *goose – geese* and *cactus – cacti*, and those that remain the same in both singular and plural form, as in *moose – moose*. To make an **irregular plural noun possessive**, add an apostrophe and *s* ('s) to the end of the irregular plural noun.

For example:

Singular Noun	Irregular Plural Noun	Irregular Plural Possessive Noun
tooth	teeth	teeth's
deer	deer	deer's
ox	oxen	oxen's

Possessive forms can be tricky in writing, but using them correctly is important to make your meaning clear. It just takes practice.

A. Circle the correct irregular plural possessive noun in each sentence.

1. The (womens' / women's) change room has six showers.

2. My (feet's / feets') achiness is probably due to my tight-fitting shoes.

3. Her (teeth's / teeths') health has improved since she started flossing daily.

4. Those (cactis' / cacti's) flowers are beautiful, but don't get too close to the plants!

5. My sister and I are responsible for cleaning out our (sheeps' / sheep's) pen.

B. Write a sentence using the possessive form of each irregular plural noun.

1. men _____

2. women _____

3. children _____

C. Write two sentences about something that belongs to something else, using irregular plural nouns.

1. _____

_____

2. _____

_____

D. Choose an irregular noun and write down the singular, plural, possessive singular, and possessive plural form of it. Then, write a sentence using each form.

USE CONCRETE AND ABSTRACT NOUNS

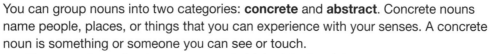

You can group nouns into two categories: **concrete** and **abstract**. Concrete nouns name people, places, or things that you can experience with your senses. A concrete noun is something or someone you can see or touch.

For example: calendar, ocean, ranch, biologist, electrician

Abstract nouns name ideas, feelings, or qualities. An abstract noun is something you cannot experience with your senses. You cannot see or touch it.

For example: fairness, year, love, intelligence, beauty, luck

Abstract nouns can convey big ideas, emotions, and concepts. But, because some abstract nouns can mean different things to different people, they can be too general and often benefit from more explanation. Think of the phrase *the park's beauty*, for example. A more precise phrase would be *the park's beautiful gardens*. Concrete nouns are generally more exact, but abstract nouns can be powerful. Always choose the best noun for your purpose.

A. Write *C* for concrete or *A* for abstract beside each noun.

1. pasture ___   **3.** creativity ___   **5.** curiosity ___   **7.** accuracy ___

2. forgiveness ___   **4.** politician ___   **6.** furniture ___   **8.** Fraser River ___

B. Identify the nouns in the following sentences. Underline the concrete nouns and circle the abstract nouns. You do not have to include pronouns.

1. My friend and I have had a long friendship, ever since we went to the same daycare in our neighbourhood.

2. My sister said that her college has buildings with gardens on their roofs, to supply food and support ecology.

3. The bus took the students around the city while their guide pointed out efforts toward sustainability.

4. Canadians have the right to live in a safe community and are expected to be responsible citizens.

C. Write two sentences, each containing an abstract noun.

1. _____

2. _____

D. Look for examples of advertisements in print or on television that use abstract nouns to help sell something. Some examples to watch for are *lifestyle*, *beauty*, *success*, and *comfort*. Choose one example and rewrite the ad, using concrete nouns to give a more precise description of what is being sold. Compare the effect of the original with your rewritten ad.

IDENTIFY A VARIETY OF VERBS

There are several types of verbs. **Action verbs** show action—something that a noun can do, such as *climb* or *travel*. They also show actions that cannot actually be seen, such as *imagine* or *assume*.

Some verbs have one or more **auxiliary verbs** (helping verbs) before the main verb: *We are deciding. He did think.* Common auxiliary verbs include forms of the verbs *be* (*am, is, are, was, were*), *do* (*do, does, did*), and *have* (*has, have, had*).

Linking verbs do not show actions. They link the subject with more information about it: *She is pleased. The surface feels smooth.* Common linking verbs include *appear, seem, smell, sound, taste, look*, and forms of the verb *be*. Take care when identifying linking verbs, because some of them can also act as action verbs: *He feels the wall. They smell the fish.*

A **phrasal verb** consists of a verb followed by another word that changes the meaning of the verb: *hand in, add up, break down, ran into*.

Part of effective writing is choosing strong, exact, and informative verbs to make your meaning clear.

A. **Underline the linking verb in each sentence. Then, circle the correct pair of words that the verb links.**

1. The photographer was satisfied with the series of prints she produced.

   a) photographer, satisfied   **b)** photographer, series   **c)** prints, she

2. The wind sounds threatening as it howls through the trees.

   a) threatening, it   **b)** wind, threatening   **c)** it, trees

3. The customers looked unhappy as they waited in the long line.

   a) they, line   **b)** customers, unhappy   **c)** customers, waited

B. **Identify whether the underlined verb in each sentence is an action verb, auxiliary verb, linking verb, or phrasal verb.**

1. I <u>looked</u> at the finish line and felt a sudden surge of energy.   _____

2. Our group <u>has</u> agreed that our report needs more research.   _____

3. The chef's vegetable dish <u>tasted</u> both salty and sweet.   _____

4. The little boy admitted he <u>made up</u> the story about his lost shoes.   _____

5. We <u>calculated</u> that the drive would be four hours.   _____

C. Write an ending for each sentence starter, using the type of verb indicated in parentheses.

1. (action verb) In an instant, the lion _____

_____.

2. (auxiliary verb) When the concert is over, the friends _____

_____.

3. (linking verb) The food _____

_____.

4. (phrasal verb) We were completely surprised when _____

_____.

D. Write two paragraphs to describe an adventure you have had. Use interesting and precise action verbs, as well as linking, auxiliary, and phrasal verbs.

_____

_____

_____

_____

_____

_____

_____

_____

_____

_____

_____

_____

_____

_____

_____

_____

_____

_____

_____

_____

LESSON 46
PROVIDE MORE INFORMATION: VERB PHRASES

A **verb phrase** consists of one or more auxiliary (helping) verbs and a main verb: *am laughing*; *might have arrived*. Common auxiliary verbs are forms of *be, do, have, can, may*, and *will*. In verb phrases, the main verb often has an *-ed* or *-ing* ending, and is called a *participle*.

A verb phrase acts as a verb, but it provides more information about the subject and its action.

　　For example:　I *will reply* soon. (shows when an action happens)
　　　　　　　　We *have been learning* about glaciers. (shows an ongoing action)
　　　　　　　　Yes, we *did eat* the whole cake. (creates emphasis)
　　　　　　　　The wheat *has ripened*. (shows a state of being or condition)

A.　Underline the verb phrase in each sentence.

　　1. I was wearing sunscreen, so I was safe.

　　2. Our class may be hosting a reception for our parents and guardians.

　　3. He seemed calm as he took the microphone, but actually he was trembling.

　　4. After years of lessons, Tai has become an excellent swimmer.

　　5. I can remember the storm as if it happened yesterday.

B.　Use each of the following verb phrases in a sentence:

could be leaving　　　had asked　　　will be trying　　　is sleeping

　　1. _____

　　2. _____

　　3. _____

　　4. _____

C.　Complete each sentence by writing a verb phrase.

　　1. When we get to the beach, we _____.

　　2. For years now, we _____ on Earth Day.

　　3. Now that it is autumn, the leaves _____.

D.　Choose two of the sentences you wrote for Exercise B. Rewrite them, this time without the auxiliary verb. Think about the differences in meaning between the original sentences and the rewritten sentences.

SHOW WHEN AN ACTION HAPPENS: VERB TENSES

You can change the form of a verb to show when an action happens—past, present, or future. The form indicates the **verb tense**. The following are some common verb tenses:

Simple present: the action is happening now, or it usually happens.
> For example: *We walk* to school.

Present progressive: the action is happening now and is ongoing in the present.
> For example: They *are paving* the main street this summer.

Simple past: the action has already happened.
> For example: She *described* her trip.

Past progressive: the action was ongoing in the past.
> For example: I *was raking* leaves yesterday.

Simple future: the action has not yet happened.
> For example: They *will graduate* this year.

In your writing, use tenses to let your readers know when an action takes place. Maintain the same tense in a piece of writing unless you have a specific reason for changing it.

A. **Identify the tense of the underlined verb in each sentence.**

1. My brother <u>was keeping</u> a journal last month to record his food choices. _____

2. Sofia <u>will fly</u> to Ottawa for training to volunteer overseas. _____

3. I <u>am listening</u> to music to help me stay calm right now. _____

4. When the career counsellor finished his talk, Anya <u>thanked</u> him. _____

5. Mom and I <u>manage</u> stress with yoga and running. _____

B. **For each sentence, fill in the line with the correct tense of the verb in parentheses. In some cases, there are several correct tenses for you to choose from.**

1. Every time I _____ my little sisters, something gets spilled. (babysit)

2. I _____ my parents the form for the workshop as soon as I can find it! (give)

3. After Stefan _____ the marine biologist, he knew what career he wanted. (interview)

4. Yesterday, I _____ when a deer suddenly bounded into our yard. (study)

5. I _____ the book for our sci-fi book club next month. (choose)

6. They played a good game but _____ every ball that came my way. (hit)

C. **Write a sentence for each verb and tense indicated. You will need to change the verb form.**

    1. *grow* – present progressive

    _____

    _____

    2. *try* – past progressive

    _____

    _____

D. **Using the simple present tense, write a short paragraph describing an exciting event you have experienced or seen. Then, rewrite your paragraph using one of the other verb tenses described in this lesson.**

    1. _____

    _____

    _____

    _____

    _____

    _____

    _____

    _____

    _____

    _____

    2. _____

    _____

    _____

    _____

    _____

    _____

    _____

    _____

    _____

    _____

E. **Identify the tense you chose for the second paragraph. Write a summary statement that explains the effects of changing verb tenses in your writing.**

MAKE THE PAST TENSE: IRREGULAR VERBS

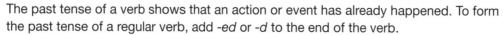

The past tense of a verb shows that an action or event has already happened. To form the past tense of a regular verb, add -ed or -d to the end of the verb.

For example: reflect – reflected; locate – located

Some verbs, called **irregular verbs**, have a special spelling for the past tense, or use a completely different word.

For example: is – was; grow – grew; bring – brought; build – built

Some verbs are the same in both the present and the past tense.

For example: cut, fit, put

A. Underline the correct past tense for each sentence.

1. The expert on online safety (gived / gave) strong warnings to keep identity information private.

2. The decorations for last month's dance (cost / costed) too much, so we will make our own next time.

3. We (seen / saw) many hornets buzzing around, so we knew there must be a nest nearby.

4. I (swung / swinged) mightily at the first pitch—and missed rather spectacularly.

5. During our hike, we each (drunk / drank) about one litre of water per hour.

B. For each sentence, write the past tense of the verb in parentheses.

1. We _____ respectfully during the Remembrance Day ceremony. (stand)

2. After seeing the documentary, we _____ more aware of our water use. (become)

3. When the first pellet of hail _____ the window, my dog was under the bed. (hit)

4. After my pen _____ in my pocket, my day just got worse. (break)

C. Write a sentence using each of the following verbs in the past tense: forget, understand, buy.

_____

_____

_____

_____

_____

_____

_____

USE PRESENT PERFECT AND PAST PERFECT TENSES

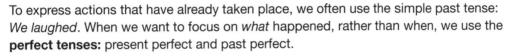

To express actions that have already taken place, we often use the simple past tense: *We laughed*. When we want to focus on *what* happened, rather than when, we use the **perfect tenses:** present perfect and past perfect.

Use the present perfect tense for actions of a non-specific time in the past, or for actions that are continuing into the present.
For example: He *has studied* all evening.

Use the past perfect tense for actions that were completed in the past before another action happened.
For example: She *had studied* for an hour before she took a break.

Perfect tenses use the past participle of the verb rather than its past tense form.
For example: *The strap had broken*—not *The strap had broke*.

A. For each set of verbs, underline the correct form for the perfect tense.

1. **a)** it consumed   **b)** it has consumed   **c)** it is consuming

2. **a)** she had written   **b)** she was writing   **c)** she had wrote

3. **a)** they chose   **b)** they had chose   **c)** they had chosen

4. **a)** I had become   **b)** I had became   **c)** I was becoming

5. **a)** we had ran   **b)** we were running   **c)** we had run

B. Underline the verb in the perfect tense in each sentence. Identify it as either present perfect (*PrP*) or past perfect (*PP*).

1. I have learned the hard way that cellphones do not float.   _____

2. Jyreese has shown impressive leadership skills this year.   _____

3. The cast had rehearsed the play many times, until they were ready.   _____

4. Mia had conducted the experiment four times before she reached a conclusion. _____

5. Before the tornado struck last year, my family had practised what to do.   _____

6. The rabbits have eaten all the lettuce we planted.   _____

C. Write one present perfect and one past perfect sentence.

PrP: _____

_____

PP: _____

_____

MATCH THE NUMBERS: SUBJECT-VERB AGREEMENT

The rule for **subject–verb agreement** is that the subject and verb in a sentence must agree (match) in number. If a subject is singular, its verb must be singular. If a subject is plural, its verb must be plural.

For example: The *lion roars*.

The *lions roar*.

Some cases are trickier, such as those in the chart below.

Case	Explanation	Example
Collective Noun	When the subject is a collective noun and is acting as one unit, the verb is singular.	My *team plays* tomorrow.
Indefinite Pronouns	Some indefinite pronouns are singular (e.g., *everyone, someone, anyone, nobody*) and take a singular verb.	*Someone is* early.
	Some indefinite pronouns are plural (e.g., *both, many*) and take a plural verb.	*Both are* early.
Compound Subjects	Subjects joined by *and* usually take a plural verb.	*Kalli and Mason are* here.
ˈles	Titles always take a singular verb.	*"The Orchards" is* my latest poem.

A. For each sent⟍ ⟍ choose the correct verb in parentheses.

1. "Canada in the ⟍s," my slideshow, _____ primary sources. (contains / contain)

2. Many _____ to hear the next band, despite the rain. (are staying / is staying)

3. Our student council ___ _____ a Water Awareness day. (are planning / is planning)

4. An apple and an energy ba⟍ _____ in my backpack, ready for our hike. (is / are)

5. Nobody _____ a sense of humour like Sam's. (have / has)

B. Underline the subject in each sentence. Circle the verb or verb phrase that agrees with it. Then, write S for singular or P for plural to describe the subject and verb.

1. Minerals and forests are two important natural resources in British Columbia. _____

2. The bowl of cherries makes a bright centrepiece for the table. _____

3. With these secret acts of kindness, someone is lifting people's spirits today. _____

4. Olympian Clara Hughes's determination and skill inspire many Canadians. _____

5. Today, this couple celebrates thirty years of marriage. _____

6. Both are experienced swimmers with years of training. _____

C. **Complete the following sentence starters. Use a present-tense verb and make sure it agrees with the subject.**

    1. Warm-ups and cool-downs _____

    _____

    2. In fact, nobody _____

    _____

    3. "O Canada" _____

    _____

D. **The following paragraph has eight errors in subject–verb agreement. Underline the incorrect verbs. Rewrite the paragraph by changing each verb to a form that agrees with its subject. Keep the verbs in the same tense as in their original form.**

Concussions is a type of brain injury that can result from hits to the head. If someone who have been hit in the head experience blurred vision, confusion, or a severe headache, he or she should be taken to the emergency department. Slurred speech and dizziness is other possible signs of concussion. If you play team sports, make sure your coaches knows the signs of concussion. Your team, as a whole, need to pay attention to any hits players receives. Share information about concussions. For example, "Protecting Brains," a safety video I made with my friend, were shown to my whole school.

_____

_____

_____

_____

_____

_____

_____

_____

_____

_____

_____

_____

_____

_____

_____

MATCH THE SUBJECT: LINKING VERBS

Linking verbs connect the subject to a word or words that describe the subject or that give more information about it. Those words are called the *subject complement*. When writing, take care to make the linking verb agree with the subject and not with the subject complement. In other words, if your subject is singular, your linking verb must be singular. If your subject is plural, your linking verb must be plural.

For example: The *theme is* human rights.

The *hats have been* a popular item at the sale.

In the first example, the subject is *theme*, which is singular, so the linking verb, *is*, must be singular. The linking verb does not have to agree with *human rights*.

In the second example, the subject is *hats*, which is plural, so the linking verb, *have been*, must be plural. The linking verb does not have to agree with *item*.

A. **In each sentence, underline the simple subject. Then, choose the verb in parentheses that agrees with the subject.**

1. The osprey _____ the official bird of Nova Scotia. (is / are)

2. An event that I would prefer to forget _____ my first piano disaster—I mean, recital. (is / are)

3. The new monuments in the park _____ a gift from the city. (is / are)

4. Her skill and guidance _____ a big help to the volunteers. (has been / have been)

5. In Haudenosaunee culture, wampum beads _____ an important form of identification and record keeping. (is / are)

6. The biggest gift that I could receive _____ your supportive messages. (is / are)

7. Food and warmth _____ on my mind after a day of ice fishing. (was / were)

B. **Complete the following sentences using a form of the verb *to be*. Make sure the subject and the linking verb agree.**

1. Trust and honesty _____

_____

2. A surprise for the children _____

_____

C. **Find five sentences in a book, magazine, or advertisement that have a form of the verb *to be*. For each sentence, think about why it is plural or singular. Write two sentences using the verb *to be*, one singular and one plural.**

UNDERSTAND ACTIVE AND PASSIVE VOICE

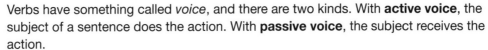

Verbs have something called *voice*, and there are two kinds. With **active voice**, the subject of a sentence does the action. With **passive voice**, the subject receives the action.

For example: The dog *chased* the squirrel. (Active voice: the subject, dog, does the action.)

The squirrel *was chased* by the dog. (Passive voice: the subject, squirrel, receives the action of being chased.)

A passive verb is always a verb phrase made up of a form of the verb *to be* plus a past participle (a verb form usually ending in *-ed* or *-en*). Other helping verbs are also used when forming the various tenses.

The general rule is to use active voice. It gives sentences more certainty, directness, and power. Passive voice can be wordy, vague, and dull. However, passive voice is useful when you want to put more emphasis on the receiver of the action, and when the person or thing doing the action is unknown or unimportant.

Note that sentences in passive voice do not always include the person or thing that does the action.

For example: The icebergs *can be viewed* from the shore.

A. For each sentence, underline the subject and circle the verb.

1. The new student was introduced by the teacher.

2. Hailey tossed her hat onto the coat rack.

3. The parents laughed at their baby's funny faces.

4. My sister is being awarded a plaque by her coaches.

5. Karif made a video of his simple hydraulic system.

6. The silo and barns were damaged by the tornado.

7. The play will be performed next week by the Drama Club.

B. Decide if the verb is in active or passive voice in each sentence. Then, write "Active" or "Passive" on the line.

1. Isaac Newton discovered the formula for the measurement of viscosity. _____

2. The fireworks' explosions were heard by people three kilometres away. _____

3. After the emergency, the family thanked the firefighters for their quick response. _____

4. That video has been seen by over five million viewers. _____

5. The Bay of Fundy has the highest tides in the world. _____

C. **Change each sentence from passive voice to active voice.**

1. An interesting artifact was discovered yesterday by an archaeologist.

   _____

2. Braden was chosen as spokesperson by the class.

   _____

3. Buoyancy experiments will be conducted by our science class next week.

   _____

4. A new logo was chosen by the committee.

   _____

D. **Write a brief paragraph describing a time when you broke something or spilled something. Use the active voice in your sentences. Then, rewrite the paragraph in the passive voice.**

Active voice: _____

_____ _____

_____ _____

_____ _____

_____ _____

_____ _____

_____ _____

_____ _____

_____

Passive voice: _____

_____

_____

_____

_____

_____

_____

_____

_____

E. **Read aloud the paragraphs you wrote for Exercise D, listening for differences in how the writing sounds and each paragraph's overall effect.**

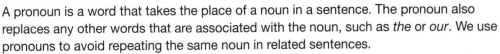

REPLACE SUBJECT NOUNS: SUBJECT PRONOUNS

A pronoun is a word that takes the place of a noun in a sentence. The pronoun also replaces any other words that are associated with the noun, such as *the* or *our*. We use pronouns to avoid repeating the same noun in related sentences.

For example: The elevator is old. The elevator shakes. (*The elevator* is repeated.)
The elevator is old. *It* shakes. (*It* takes the place of *the elevator*.)

A **subject pronoun** takes the place of the noun that is the subject of the sentence. It tells who or what the sentence is about. Subject pronouns can be singular (*I, you, she, he,* and *it*) or plural (*you, we,* and *they*). The subject pronoun often, but not always, appears at the beginning of a sentence. The subject pronoun can also replace a compound subject.

For example: *Aidan* and *Dev* are late. *They* might miss the bus.
(*They* replaces *Aidan and Dev*.)

Note that *they* can be used as a gender-neutral singular pronoun. Other gender-neutral singular pronouns that have been used in recent years include *ze, xe,* and *ne*.

A. **Complete each sentence by replacing the subject in parentheses with a subject pronoun.**

1. _____ are badminton partners. (Brodie and Mirsad)

2. _____ has a population of over 1.6 million. (The city of Montréal)

3. _____ met at a sports camp last summer. (Your cousin and I)

4. _____ can help plan our meals for the week. (You and your brother)

B. **Underline the subject pronoun in each sentence.**

1. You should be very proud of your achievements in the fitness program.

2. As soon as the sun rose, we put our canoes in the water.

3. It was a sad time for my community when the historic city hall was torn down.

4. After the movie was over, he stayed in his seat, still in awe.

5. For many years, they have shared many adventures.

C. **After each sentence, write a related follow-up sentence. Start the sentence with a subject pronoun that replaces the subject of the first sentence.**

1. My running shoes are soaked. _____

_____

2. Our laptop needs to be repaired. _____

_____

REPLACE OBJECT NOUNS: OBJECT PRONOUNS

A pronoun is a word that takes the place of a noun in a sentence. An **object pronoun** takes the place of an object noun. An object noun or pronoun shows what or who is receiving an action, and usually follows an action verb. You can use object pronouns to avoid unnecessary repetition of the noun.

For example: The dog caught the toy and chewed *the toy*.
The dog caught the toy and chewed *it*.

An object pronoun can also follow a preposition, such as *to, from, with, for,* or *about*.
For example: I miss my friend. I have not heard *from her*.

The object pronouns are *me, you* (singular and plural), *him, her, it, us,* and *them*. With the pronouns *me* and *I*, remember that *me* is the object pronoun and *I* is the subject pronoun.
For example: Please give your registration to *her or me*. (not *to her or I*)

A. Underline the object pronoun in each sentence and circle the object noun (or nouns) that it replaces. There are other pronouns in the sentences, so choose carefully.

1. I like yoga, and my flexibility has increased because of it.

2. Cody lost his sunscreen and hat, and, on this hot day, he needs to find them soon.

3. Our grandmother told my brother and me that she will take us to meet our relatives in Italy.

4. Reading is a challenge for my little sister, so I work with her every day.

5. Our school honours our war veterans simply by taking time to remember them.

B. Complete each sentence by choosing the object pronoun that replaces the object in the sentence.

1. I respect Aunt Lisa, whose volunteer work is very important to _____. (me / I).

2. In Tofino, Dad booked a whale watching tour for us. We absolutely loved _____. (it / them)

3. Our failed attempts at snowboarding embarrassed my friend and me. But nobody even

   noticed _____. (we / us)

4. The bike accident injured both my brother and me. The recovery was difficult for

   _____. (us / I)

5. My aunt adopted a baby boy, and we are so happy to have _____ in our family. (he / him)

C. Choose two sentences from Exercise A and rewrite them, this time repeating the object rather than using the object pronoun. Read both versions aloud a couple of times to hear how they sound.

SHOW OWNERSHIP: POSSESSIVE PRONOUNS

A pronoun takes the place of a noun in a sentence. Like some nouns, some pronouns show ownership—they show that something belongs to someone or something. We call these **possessive pronouns**. They can be singular (*mine, yours, his, hers*) or plural (*ours, yours, theirs*). Unlike possessive adjectives, such as *my, your, his,* and *our,* possessive pronouns do not modify nouns or noun phrases. They stand alone.

Note that *theirs* can be used as a gender-neutral possessive pronoun. Other gender-neutral possessive pronouns that have been used in recent years include *zirs, xyrs,* and *nirs.*

> For example: Are those notebooks *yours*?
> *Mine* is a knitted hat, and *hers* is flannel.
> I have my chores, and my brother has *his*.

Note that you do not add an apostrophe to form possessive pronouns.

A. For each possessive adjective in the left column, write the possessive pronoun form to complete the sentence in the right column.

1. my umbrella   The umbrella is _____.

2. your theory   The theory is _____.

3. their province   The province is _____.

4. our heritage   The heritage is _____.

5. his knowledge   The knowledge is _____.

B. Complete each sentence by adding a possessive pronoun that fits logically.

1. I will take the blame for the mistake, because the fault was all _____.

2. My research is done, but Rachel feels unsure about _____, so she intends to find more sources.

3. I forgot my battery charger, so do you mind if I use _____, if you have one?

4. The dance club members are doing most of the work for our fundraiser, so we think the decision about the theme should be _____.

5. The water was seeping into our neighbours' apartment, but not into _____.

C. Skim a book, magazine, or newspaper to find examples of possessive pronouns. For three of them, figure out whom the possessive pronoun refers to. Is there always a reference? Why was a possessive pronoun used in each case?

USE INDEFINITE PRONOUNS

Some pronouns refer to people or things that are not specific. We call these **indefinite pronouns**.

Singular indefinite pronouns include *another, anybody, anything, each, everything, everybody, somebody, someone, something, nothing, less, little, other,* and *much.*
  For example: *Something* is missing in this recipe.

Plural indefinite pronouns include *others, several, many, few, fewer,* and *both.*
  For example: *Both* are good ideas.

A singular pronoun takes a singular verb, and a plural pronoun takes a plural verb. Some indefinite pronouns, such as *all, any,* and *more,* can be either singular or plural— singular if they refer to something that is singular or non-countable, and plural if they refer to something plural.
  For example: *All* of my patience *is* gone. (singular)
             All of our cookies *are* gone. (plural)

A. Choose the indefinite pronoun that correctly completes each sentence.

1. Fifty people attended the community picnic this year—_____ than last year. (few / fewer)

2. The store offers free food samples, and I have already had _____! (several / any)

3. Some Canadians prefer coastal environments while _____ prefer flat lands, like the Prairies. (everybody / others)

4. Overall, _____ did well on the theory portion of the music course, while others did better with performance. (some / anyone)

5. Even very young Métis children—the "tiny tots"—take part in the Grand Entry at the competition powwow, while _____ watches. (everyone / all)

B. Underline the indefinite pronoun in each sentence. Then choose the verb that agrees with it.

1. All of the members of the Eco Club (is going / are going) to a weekend conference.

2. Both of those cities (is / are) capital cities.

3. If there (is / are) any appetizers left, I would love to try them.

4. I did a lot of studying, but more (was / were) required for that test!

5. I don't think that anything (makes / make) me happier than a hug from my baby brother.

C. Find three examples of indefinite pronouns in advertisements, in books, or on websites. Write down the examples, then identify whether each pronoun is plural or singular.

DESCRIBE NOUNS: RELATIVE PRONOUNS

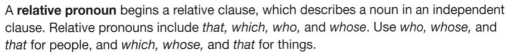

A **relative pronoun** begins a relative clause, which describes a noun in an independent clause. Relative pronouns include *that, which, who,* and *whose.* Use *who, whose,* and *that* for people, and *which, whose,* and *that* for things.

For example: The girl *who* performs next is my cousin.
I found the book *that* I needed.

In the first example, *who* begins the relative clause *who performs next* and describes the noun *girl*. In the second example, *that* begins the relative clause *that I needed* and describes the noun *book*.

A relative clause can identify the noun by giving essential information about it, or it can simply give non-essential information about the noun. If it identifies the noun, do not use commas before and after the relative clause. If the relative clause gives non-essential information, do use commas before and after.

For example: The book *that is on the table* is mine. (essential information)
Her dog, *which is a beagle*, is lively. (non-essential information)

Note that if you have to choose between using *that* or *which,* always use *that* in an essential clause (no commas) and *which* in a non-essential clause (with commas).

A. **Underline the relative clause in each sentence and write the relative pronoun on the line.**

1. For dessert, let's have the cake that Sasha made.   _____

2. I would like to meet the woman who knew my great-grandmother.   _____

3. That cat, whose name is Abby, will entertain you for hours.   _____

4. The mechanic who fixed our car was born in Nova Scotia.   _____

5. Our apartment, which is on the fifth floor, has two bedrooms.   _____

6. The spice that she likes best is nutmeg.   _____

B. **Complete each sentence by choosing a relative pronoun from the following list:**

who   whose   that   which

1. The woman _____ is giving the speech is an expert on earthquakes.

2. I found out that our bus driver, _____ name is Chris, plays in a band.

3. Did you know that my uncle, _____ is my mother's brother, is a pilot?

4. The winds, _____ are coming from the north, are very strong.

5. The bridge _____ links Prince Edward Island and New Brunswick is the Confederation Bridge.

6. We learned that fluids, _____ are substances that flow, include gases.

7. The artist _____ work I admire most is Emily Carr.

MAKE PRONOUNS AND ANTECEDENTS AGREE

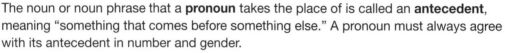

The noun or noun phrase that a **pronoun** takes the place of is called an **antecedent**, meaning "something that comes before something else." A pronoun must always agree with its antecedent in number and gender.

For example: I hugged my *sister* and told *her* I was sorry.
(The noun *sister* is the antecedent of the pronoun *her*.)
My two *friends* are away, and *they* miss home.
(The noun *friends* is the antecedent of the pronoun *they*.)
The dogs next to us think that our yard is *theirs*.
(The noun phrase *the dogs next to us* is the antecedent of the pronoun *theirs*.)
Charlotte can do this *herself*.
(The noun *Charlotte* is the antecedent of the pronoun *herself*.)

Note that *they* can be used as a gender-neutral singular pronoun. Other gender-neutral singular pronouns that have been used in recent years include *ze, xe*, and *ne*.

A. **In each sentence, circle the pronoun and underline its antecedent.**

1. Evan borrowed a pen and then lost it.

2. The cats were tripping over themselves to get to the food dish.

3. Kyra and Shane are writing a song they want to perform for the school.

4. Zohar knows that, with the next point, the trophy could be his.

5. After blaming friends and family, the girl finally realized the mistake was hers.

6. You and Riley should be proud of the way you helped the younger students today.

B. **Complete each sentence by adding a pronoun that agrees with its antecedent, which is underlined. Choose a pronoun that makes sense with the antecedent and the sentence context.**

1. Every day <u>I</u> like to challenge _____ to do something nice for someone.

2. <u>The forest fire</u> is spreading rapidly, and _____ shows no sign of burning out.

3. If you forgot your binoculars, <u>Matthew</u> will loan you _____.

4. These students presented their project, so could <u>you and Sadiya</u> now present _____?

5. <u>My friend and I</u> had an argument, but _____ talked things over and worked it out.

6. I try to have a positive self-image, but <u>some young people</u> judge _____ too harshly.

7. After the tournament, we congratulated <u>our opponents</u> and gave _____ a small gift.

8. Please watch <u>my sister and me</u> at the dance competition, and be sure to cheer for _____.

USE A VARIETY OF PRONOUNS AND ANTECEDENTS

The important thing to remember about **pronouns** and **antecedents** (the nouns or noun phrases that pronouns take the place of) is that they must always agree. If the antecedent is singular, the pronoun must be singular. If the antecedent is plural, the pronoun must be plural. If the antecedent is masculine or feminine, the pronoun must agree in gender.

For example: *She* wrapped *herself* in a cozy blanket.
Cal and Shawn are tired; *both* stayed up too late.

Note that *they* can be used as a gender-neutral singular pronoun. Other gender-neutral singular pronouns that have been used in recent years include *ze, xe,* and *ne.*

A. **In each sentence, circle the pronoun that replaces the underlined antecedent.**

1. Mary Ann Shadd settled in Windsor, Ontario, where she published an anti-slavery newspaper.

2. Manuel's birthday is tomorrow, and the whole day will be his to enjoy.

3. Inuit Tapiriit Kanatami represents Inuit and works to resolve the issues and challenges facing them.

4. People in the massive crowd were crushed together, and many suffered heat exhaustion.

5. You and I could find ourselves in danger if the waves keep hitting the boat.

6. When I saw the stack of dishes from the hallway, I said to Dad, "Let me help you with those."

7. Her cello, which was purchased in Paris, is made from carbon fibre.

B. **In each sentence, underline the correct pronoun. Make sure each one agrees with its antecedent.**

1. Tyrese seemed fairly pleased with (himself / oneself) when his presentation was over.

2. We are not sure how many people were injured in the accident, but paramedics treated (some / fewer) on the scene.

3. Something is in the bushes, rustling around, but I can't see (them / it).

4. If you want to build your confidence, (yourself / you) need a more positive outlook.

5. (That / These) are the only two books by this author that I have not read.

C. **The following sentence has an error in pronoun–antecedent agreement. Write a corrected version of the sentence.**

When people conduct science experiments, you should wear protective gear.

_____

_____

WRITE DESCRIPTIVE WORDS: ADJECTIVES

An **adjective** is a word that modifies a noun. Adjectives add detail and description to help readers picture or sense what they are reading.

There are different types of adjectives. In addition to the descriptive adjectives we normally think of (*community* centre, *Métis* history), there are the following categories:

Demonstrative adjectives point out specific people or things. The demonstrative adjectives are *this*, *these*, *that*, and *those*. We use *this* and *these* to refer to objects close by, and *that* and *those* for objects further away.
> For example: *This* store is advertised on *that* billboard.

Possessive adjectives indicate who or what owns something. The possessive adjectives are *my*, *your*, *his*, *her*, *our*, and *their*.
> For example: *Our* dog loves playing with *your* cat.

Interrogative adjectives modify nouns that are used in questions. The interrogative adjectives are *which*, *what*, and *whose*.
> For example: *Which* day is Raj arriving?

A. Write an appropriate demonstrative adjective for each sentence.

1. It's late, but I have to read another chapter. I love _____ book.

2. _____ clouds over there look threatening. I think it's going to rain.

3. Do you like _____ bracelets I'm wearing? I made them!

B. Write a possessive adjective for each sentence.

1. David is late, and I can't reach _____ cellphone.

2. Jamila should open a restaurant, because _____ pie is the best I've ever had.

3. I can't get a decent shot on net. I think _____ scoring streak is over.

C. Write an appropriate interrogative adjective for each sentence.

1. _____ food are you bringing to the potluck?

2. _____ red car is being towed?

3. _____ band is playing first at the concert?

D. Underline the adjectives in each sentence. (Do not include the articles *the* or *a*.)

1. This pamphlet outlines various projects by government agencies for providing clean water.

2. Whose safety glasses were left on the storage cupboard for the power tools?

3. Wolverines live in Arctic regions, using their large, furry paws like snowshoes.

E. In each sentence, add two adjectives to modify the noun in italics. Choose adjectives that help your readers picture what you describe.

1. The queen looked down at the _____ , _____ *crowd*.

2. My favourite movie features a/an _____ , _____ *character*.

3. After finishing the race, Sammy had a/an _____ , _____ *feeling*.

4. Sasha and her friends went to the _____ , _____ *festival*.

5. We just moved to this _____ , _____ *neighbourhood*.

F. Write a descriptive paragraph on a topic of your choice, using a variety of descriptive adjectives. Circle the descriptive adjectives in your writing.

_____

_____

_____

_____

_____

_____

_____

_____

_____

_____

_____

_____

_____

_____

_____

_____

_____

_____

_____

_____

_____

_____

_____

MAKE COMPARISONS: ADJECTIVES

LESSON 61

An **adjective** has two different forms for making comparisons: comparative (for comparing two things) and superlative (for comparing three or more things).

The chart below shows how to form different types of adjectives into adjectives that make comparisons.

Types of Adjectives	Positive	Comparative	Superlative
regular, one syllable	great	greater	greatest
one syllable ending in a consonant with a single vowel before it	big	bigger	biggest
two syllables ending in a consonant that is followed by the letter *y*	hungry	hungrier	hungriest
two or more syllables, other cases	delicate natural	more delicate less natural	most delicate least natural

A. **For each adjective on the left, choose the correct comparative or superlative form from the two options on the right. Underline your choice.**

1. certain   less certainer / least certain

2. blue   bluer / bluier

3. famous   famouser / more famous

4. mighty   most mightiest / mightiest

5. small   less smallest / smaller

6. sad   sadder / more sadder

B. **On each line, write the correct form of the adjective in parentheses. Do not use *less* or *least*.**

1. This paint colour looks _____ in the sunlight. (red)

2. Between Emma and her sister, Emma is _____. (quiet)

3. Our grey cat is friendly, the calico is friendlier, and the black one is the _____. (friendly)

4. This restaurant is _____ than the other one. (expensive)

5. After that explanation, I feel _____ than before! (confused)

C. **Find some sentences from songs or advertisements that contain adjectives. Experiment with changing the adjectives to different forms; for example, change the comparative form to the regular form, or change the regular form to the superlative form.**

98   Grasp Grammar and Usage

Copyright © 2019 by Nelson Education Ltd.

DESCRIBE ACTIONS: ADVERBS

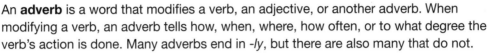

An **adverb** is a word that modifies a verb, an adjective, or another adverb. When modifying a verb, an adverb tells how, when, where, how often, or to what degree the verb's action is done. Many adverbs end in *-ly*, but there are also many that do not.
> For example: He smiled *broadly*. They walked *fast*.

When modifying an adjective or adverb, an adverb makes the meaning more precise.
> For example: I saw the *very* small car. (modifies the adjective *small*)
> He sings *quite* well. (modifies the adverb *well*)

An adverb phrase is a group of two or more adverbs that act as an adverb.
> For example: She poured the hot liquid *extremely slowly*.
> They lined up for the roller coaster *excitedly and nervously*.

In your writing, use a variety of adverbs to provide specific information about actions and to make your writing interesting, descriptive, and lively.

A. **Underline all the adverbs in each sentence. The number in parentheses tells you how many adverbs there are.**

1. I carefully calculated the area of the rectangle and recorded it confidently. (2)

2. We occasionally see porcupines, but they usually stay away. (3)

3. The very cold weather caused us to stamp our feet briskly and quickly move inside. (4)

4. The rain fell hard, and soon the river rose dangerously. (3)

B. **Underline the adverb phrase in each sentence. Circle the verb that it modifies.**

1. Cars pass constantly and endlessly on this stretch of the Trans-Canada Highway.

2. The soccer referee used yellow cards very often in that game.

3. With a torn knee ligament, I limped slowly and painfully.

C. **Rewrite each sentence by adding adverbs that tell how, when, how often, or to what degree the action is done.**

1. The sun shone.

_____

_____

2. The boat capsized.

_____

_____

LESSON 63

WRITE DESCRIPTIVELY: ADJECTIVES AND ADVERBS

Adjectives modify nouns and pronouns. **Adverbs** modify verbs, adjectives, and other adverbs. Both play an essential role in writing. They provide precise, interesting details, and descriptions that help readers understand and picture exactly what you mean. They can make your writing livelier and more vivid.

You can tell an adjective from an adverb by figuring out what the word is doing or describing. You can also consider what questions the word is answering. Adverbs often answer the questions *How? When? Where?* and *To what extent?* Adjectives often answer the questions *What kind? Which?* or *How many?*

Knowing when to use *bad* or *badly* and *good* or *well* is important. *Bad* and *good* are adjectives so they describe nouns; *badly* and *well* are adverbs so they modify verbs.

For example: I ate a *bad* meal.   He is a *good* person.   (adjectives)
I played *badly*.   I did *well* on the test.   (adverbs)

A. **For each sentence, decide whether the underlined word is an adjective or an adverb. Write *ADJ* or *ADV* on the line.**

1. I had a <u>bad</u> feeling when I saw how thin the ice was on the pond.   _____

2. When I sit <u>straight</u> during yoga, I can breathe more deeply.   _____

3. It has been such a <u>long</u> time since I have seen you.   _____

4. She returned from the game with a <u>hoarse</u> voice.   _____

B. **Change each adjective in parentheses to an adverb.**

1. He hoped that now they would treat him _____. (different)

2. She performed _____. (good)

3. I am speaking _____. (sincere)

4. Why are you behaving so _____? (immature)

C. **Use adjectives and adverbs to make each sentence more descriptive. Use at least one adjective and one adverb per sentence.**

1. She ate her lunch.

_____

_____

2. The waves came in.

_____

_____

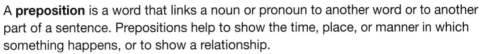

SHOW RELATIONSHIPS: PREPOSITIONS

A **preposition** is a word that links a noun or pronoun to another word or to another part of a sentence. Prepositions help to show the time, place, or manner in which something happens, or to show a relationship.

For example: We walked *near* the river.

In the example, the preposition *near* connects the noun *river* with the verb *walked*.

Some of the most common prepositions are *up*, *down*, *at*, *to*, *on*, *in*, *for*, *with*, *off*, *of*, *by*, and *from*. Some other examples are *above*, *along*, *around*, *behind*, *beyond*, *inside*, *outside*, *excluding*, *past*, and *toward*.

A. **Underline the prepositions in each sentence. The numbers in parentheses tell you how many prepositions there are in each sentence.**

  1. Excluding taxes, the price of the jacket was still over my budget. (3)

  2. For dinner, we walked down the street from our apartment to a popular Thai restaurant. (4)

  3. Once inside the National Gallery of Canada, we toured the first floor, admiring works by Inuit artists. (3)

  4. Our cat sneaked outside our townhouse and visited the neighbours who live around the corner from us, past the elm tree. (4)

B. **In each sentence, choose the better preposition of the two options provided. Write your choice on the line.**

  1. The trees _____ that stretch of the river are willows. (along / on)

  2. Our class often discusses safety guidelines _____ using online communications. (with / for)

  3. Early the next morning, the expedition set off _____ the mountain's summit. (toward / beyond)

  4. That movie was _____ weird! (behind / beyond)

  5. We found one nervous contestant hiding _____ the stage curtain. (at / behind)

C. **Write two sentences. In each sentence, use at least two prepositions.**

  _____

  _____

  _____

  _____

D. **Select a paragraph from a book, magazine, or website. Read it, then list all the prepositions used in the paragraph.**

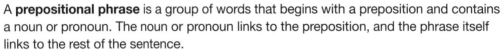

DESCRIBE A NOUN: PREPOSITIONAL PHRASES

A **prepositional phrase** is a group of words that begins with a preposition and contains a noun or pronoun. The noun or pronoun links to the preposition, and the phrase itself links to the rest of the sentence.

> For example: Sami fell asleep *during the movie*.

In the example, the preposition *during* links to the noun *movie*; the prepositional phrase *during the movie* tells when Sami fell asleep.

Prepositional phrases can act as adverbs or as adjectives. They help to explain, for example, where, how, when, why, or to what extent something happens, or which one something is.

> For example: Let's meet *by the fountain*. (tells where)
> We need to be home *before dusk*. (tells when)
> She was touched *by the community's kindness*. (tells why)
> The team *in the red jerseys* won. (tells which one)

A. **Underline the prepositional phrases in each sentence. The number in parentheses tells you how many prepositional phrases there are.**

1. They walked along the waterfront until sunset and then hopped onto a bus for home. (4)

2. Near our farm, beyond the wheat fields, stands a small forest of mainly deciduous trees. (3)

3. Through our research, we are learning about sustainability in human communities. (3)

4. During our buoyancy experiment in science class, Madeline accidentally dropped a big rock into the water, from quite a height—nobody was dry until the end of the next class. (6)

5. Tariq is going to the Laurentians in Québec for a ski trip and to visit family. (3)

6. At the Teslin Tlingit Heritage Centre, a celebration of Tlingit culture takes place biennially, in the summer. (3)

B. **Complete each of the sentence starters by adding a prepositional phrase according to the directions in parentheses. Be sure to begin your phrase with a preposition.**

1. They held the party _____. (tell when)

2. She set up her tent _____. (tell where)

3. Look at the little boy _____. (tell which one)

4. Darkness fell as the sun dropped _____. (tell why)

5. Let's practise _____. (tell when)

DESCRIBE A NOUN: PARTICIPLE PHRASES

A participle is a form of a verb that can be used as an adjective. Present participles end in *-ing*, as in *pulling*. Past participles often end in *-ed*, as in *flooded*, or *-en*, as in *broken*. A **participle phrase** is a group of words that begins with a participle and acts as an adjective. It describes a noun or pronoun.

If you place the phrase right after the noun and the information is essential to the meaning of the sentence, do not put a comma before or after the phrase.

> For example: The man *holding the baby* is my uncle.
> (The participle phrase *holding the baby* describes the noun *man.*)

You can also place a participle phrase at the beginning of a sentence.

> For example: *Swarmed by bees*, we quickly took cover.
> (The participle phrase *Swarmed by bees* describes the pronoun *we.*)

If you place the phrase at the beginning of a sentence, put a comma after the phrase.

Participle phrases are an effective way of providing description and can be useful for varying beginnings of sentences.

A. **In each sentence, underline the participle phrase. Then, circle the noun or pronoun that it describes.**

   1. Breathing deeply, the competitor prepared for her first dive.

   2. The items gathered for the yard sale are still in good condition.

   3. Shaken by his fall, the cyclist picked up his bike and kissed his helmet thankfully.

B. **Complete each sentence by adding a participle phrase. You may use a present or past participle.**

   1. _____, he climbed the steep hill.

   2. The tall girl _____ is my neighbour.

C. **Use each participle phrase in a sentence. You may place it at the beginning of the sentence or elsewhere. Remember to use punctuation correctly.**

   1. swimming close to shore

   _____

   _____

   2. injured on the field

   _____

   _____

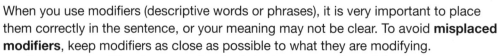

BE CLEAR: MISPLACED MODIFIERS

When you use modifiers (descriptive words or phrases), it is very important to place them correctly in the sentence, or your meaning may not be clear. To avoid **misplaced modifiers**, keep modifiers as close as possible to what they are modifying.

For example: The *sharp* woodworker's tools are stored carefully. ✗
The woodworker's *sharp* tools are stored carefully. ✓
The guide showed a black bear to the tourist *with her cubs*. ✗
The guide showed a black bear *with her cubs* to the tourist. ✓

Be aware that placement of some modifiers, such as *only*, *just*, and *nearly*, can result in very different meanings. Place these modifiers in front of the words they modify.

For example: We *just* asked him to rake the front lawn.
We asked him to rake *just* the front lawn.

The first sentence above means that we asked him seconds ago. The second sentence means that we asked him to rake the front lawn and nothing else.

A. **The underlined words in each sentence are misplaced modifiers. Rewrite each sentence, placing the modifier in a position that makes more sense. In your new sentence, circle the word being modified.**

   1. A firefighter was rescuing a cat <u>in full uniform</u>.

   _____

   2. The store clerk apologized for the mistake he made <u>kindly</u>.

   _____

   3. We feel sorry for our <u>barking</u> neighbour's dog.

   _____

   4. Dad said that we could roast marshmallows later <u>in the canoe</u>.

   _____

B. **Read the questions, then place a check mark on the line beside the correct answer.**

   1. Which sentence means she has not actually missed her bus?

   ___ She nearly missed her bus ten times.   ___ She missed her bus nearly ten times.

   2. Which sentence means that nobody but Kiera liked the dessert?

   ___ Only Kiera liked the dessert.   ___ Kiera liked only the dessert.

C. **Write two funny examples of misplaced modifiers. Then, write correct versions of your sentences.**

LESSON 68 BE CLEAR: MISPLACED AND DANGLING MODIFIERS

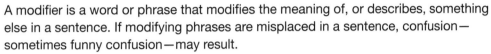

A modifier is a word or phrase that modifies the meaning of, or describes, something else in a sentence. If modifying phrases are misplaced in a sentence, confusion—sometimes funny confusion—may result.

For example: We saw the cattle *coming out of the house*.

The cattle are *not* coming out of the house! To fix a **misplaced modifier**, place it as close as possible to the word it modifies—in this case, *we*.

For example: *Coming out of the house*, we saw the cattle.

A related problem is the **dangling modifier**. A modifier "dangles" when it is meant for a word that is not actually in the sentence.

For example: *Waiting in line for tickets*, the skies darkened.

The skies are *not* waiting in line for tickets. To fix a dangling modifier, include the word it modifies. Also add any other words that are needed.

For example: *As I was* waiting in line for tickets, the skies darkened.

A. The following sentences have misplaced modifiers. Reorder each sentence and write the corrected versions on the lines below. Remember to use punctuation correctly.

1. They saw a deer and her two fawns sketching in the art studio.

_____

2. Slowly emerging from the pond scum, we watched the snapping turtle.

_____

3. On a thin layer of chocolate wafer, the chef served raspberries and cream.

_____

B. The following sentences have dangling modifiers. Write correct versions on the lines below. You can change words, add other words, and/or change the word order.

1. Waving goodbye at the airport, her suitcase was stolen.

_____

2. Diving off the high board, Earth seemed to stop moving.

_____

3. Soaking up the warm October sun, their worries were forgotten.

_____

LESSON 69
USE JOINING WORDS: CONJUNCTIONS

A **conjunction** is a word that joins elements such as words, phrases, or clauses in a sentence. Coordinating conjunctions such as *and, or, but, so*, and *yet* are used to connect similar elements in a sentence.

> For example: We finished the experiment *and* recorded the results.

A subordinating conjunction joins a subordinate clause to an independent clause. The clause introduced by the subordinating conjunction is dependent on the independent clause; it tells something about the independent clause but cannot stand on its own. Examples of subordinating conjunctions are *after, before, when, while, because, so that, since, where, if, unless, whenever*, and *although*.

> For example: I will see you tonight *unless* you need to study.

You can place a subordinate clause before or after the independent clause. If you put it before the independent clause, always follow it with a comma.

A. In each sentence, underline the conjunction. Identify the type of conjunction by writing *C* for coordinating conjunction or *S* for subordinating conjunction on the line.

1. Our volunteer firefighters are ready to help whenever our community needs them. _____

2. Because the drought was long and severe, the area's water table has been dropping. _____

3. Optical tools such as the microscope and telescope are invaluable to scientific study. _____

4. Although my speaking skills are improving, I need to work on feeling confident. _____

5. The owner claims the store is wheelchair accessible, yet Anika had difficulty getting in. _____

B. Complete each sentence starter by adding a subordinate clause that begins with a subordinating conjunction.

1. Ty raised the Canadian flag _____

2. We came in second _____

3. I lost my cellphone again _____

C. Write two sentences, with each sentence containing a coordinating conjunction.

1. _____

2. _____

D. Select two sentences from Exercises A, B, or C. Rewrite each sentence without the conjunction (the sentence should still be correct). How did the sentence have to change?

_____

_____

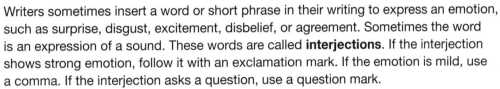

LESSON 70

EXPRESS EMOTIONS: INTERJECTIONS

Writers sometimes insert a word or short phrase in their writing to express an emotion, such as surprise, disgust, excitement, disbelief, or agreement. Sometimes the word is an expression of a sound. These words are called **interjections**. If the interjection shows strong emotion, follow it with an exclamation mark. If the emotion is mild, use a comma. If the interjection asks a question, use a question mark.

For example: *Woohoo!* My invention actually works!
Uh-oh, I think I left the lights on again.
Huh? What is going on here?

Other examples of interjections are *yes*, *no*, *what*, *so*, *ugh*, *aww*, *oh my gosh*, *mmm*, *yippee*, *really*, *brr*, and *oh yeah*.

Use interjections to convey emotion, create voice, and give your writing some liveliness and variety—but be aware that too many can be less effective.

A. **For each sentence, choose the appropriate interjection. Add the punctuation you think should appear after the interjection.**

1. _____ You didn't get me a concert ticket? (Yeah / What)

2. _____ I don't think racoons make good pets. (Brr / No)

3. _____ This place smells horrible, and it's filthy! (Ugh / So)

4. _____ I almost forgot to tell you—a parcel came for you today. (Aww / Oh yeah)

5. _____ This has to be done right now? (Really / Yippee)

6. _____ those kittens in the videos are so adorable. (What / Aww)

B. **Complete each sentence by adding an appropriate interjection and punctuation. Use interjections from this lesson or other interjections that you think of.**

1. _____ This arena is so cold!

2. _____ I have never had such a delicious meal.

C. **Complete each sentence with an idea that works with the interjection provided.**

1. Mmm, _____

2. Oh my gosh! _____

D. **Think of and list two other interjections that express a sound, such as *ugh* and *aww*. Write a sentence for each interjection. Try the sentences without the interjections and think about how effective the interjections are.**

_____

_____

BE CAREFUL: AVOID DOUBLE NEGATIVES

Some words are positive and some words are negative, as in these opposites: *anybody–nobody, any–none, anywhere–nowhere*. Verbs can also have a negative form: *have–have not, did–did not, will–won't*.

Writers usually take care to avoid the **double negative**, which results from combining two negative words in the same sentence. It is better to combine a negative and a positive.

For example: I *did not* see *nothing*. (*did not* and *nothing* are both negatives) ✗
I *did not* see *anything*. (*did not* is a negative and *anything* is a positive) ✓

Ironically, two negatives actually form a positive; for example, if you did not do nothing, then you must have done something. Therefore, if you use a double negative, your sentence actually says the opposite of what you intended. To avoid double negatives, simply choose your words carefully.

A. **The sentences on the left have double negatives. Change each sentence by switching the second negative word to a positive.**

1. I have not got none. _____

2. We don't need no help. _____

3. Don't tell nobody. _____

4. I can't find my pen nowhere. _____

5. She won't find nothing. _____

6. Do not call me no more. _____

B. **For each sentence, choose the word in parentheses that avoids the use of a double negative.**

1. Nobody _____ enter through this door. (can / can't)

2. The detectives didn't find _____ evidence at the crime scene. (no / any)

3. Nothing _____ change in the next few weeks. (will / will not)

4. I just can't find my wallet _____ (nowhere / anywhere).

5. We _____ heard nothing from our grandparents lately. (haven't / have)

6. It's true—you two _____ have absolutely nothing in common! (do / do not)

C. **Think of some double negatives used in song titles or lyrics, or times you have heard them used in informal English, or slang. Why do you think they were used? What effect do they have?**

SECTION REVIEW

A. Underline the nouns in each sentence. Do not include pronouns.

1. Auntie Asha is vice-principal of the school my cousins go to in Calgary.

2. Volunteers in our neighbourhood collect books to donate to communities that need them.

3. My sister is upset because the swimming pool is closed for maintenance for one month.

4. In our town, the fireworks on Canada Day are wonderful, but they send many dogs into distress.

5. The Canadian Paralympic Committee has a website with information about Parasport.

B. Write four sentences. The first should include a common noun, the second should include a proper noun, the third should include a collective noun, and the fourth should include a compound noun. Circle these four nouns.

1. _____

2. _____

3. _____

4. _____

C. Consider the underlined verb in each sentence. Identify whether it is an action verb, auxiliary verb, linking verb, or phrasal verb.

1. I <u>wonder</u> if I encourage other people enough in sports. _____

2. Our school band <u>sounds</u> smooth tonight. _____

3. When I <u>handed in</u> my report, I felt confident about my work. _____

4. When I <u>smelled</u> the onions cooking, I knew dinner would soon be ready. _____

5. We <u>were</u> deciding which mapping program to use when the alarm went off. _____

D. In each sentence, underline the verb in the correct tense.

1. When we decide on our topic, we (will begin / began) our research.

2. They (are writing / wrote) a play last year about life in a rural community.

3. On our trip through Canada's Prairies, we (seen / saw) the bluest skies I've ever seen.

4. She (brought / brang) the interview she recorded of her Kookum telling stories of the Ojibway.

5. I (was skateboarding / skateboarded) when a cat suddenly ran into my path and startled me.

E. Underline the subject in each sentence. Circle the verb or verb phrase that agrees with it. Then, on the short line, write _S_ for singular or _P_ for plural to describe the subject and verb.

1. "Polar Ice-Caps" is the title of my research project, which I will start today. _____

2. Someone is calling my number by mistake. _____

3. Recycling and composting are important practices in our school. _____

4. Many have seen this movie more than twice. _____

F. Fill in each blank with the correct relative pronoun from the list.

who   whose   that   which

1. The singer _____ microphone failed during the show handled the problem well.

2. The instructor _____ taught us the traditional dance is from Colombia.

3. Our video, _____ we shot in five days, is about valuing diversity.

4. The career _____ interests me the most right now is broadcast journalism.

G. In each sentence, circle the pronoun and underline its antecedent.

1. I caught the ball, then fumbled it.

2. You seem proud of yourself today—what happened?

3. Amy and LaShawn should be happy with the way they inspired the class today.

4. When I read that the forest fires were spreading, I wondered what could be done to stop them.

5. Uncle Marco lives in New Brunswick, where he works in forestry management.

H. Decide whether each underlined word below is an adjective or an adverb. Write "Adjective" or "Adverb" on the line.

1. She swam <u>well</u> in the 100-metre freestyle event. _____

2. I tried coffee when I was very young, and I thought it had a <u>bad</u> taste. _____

3. We <u>frequently</u> drive to Montréal to visit my dad's brother. _____

4. Ms. Santos said her class behaved <u>badly</u> on the field trip. _____

5. Mechanized farm equipment plants crops in very <u>straight</u> rows. _____

I. Rewrite the sentence, using adjectives and adverbs to make them more descriptive. Use at least one adjective and one adverb per sentence.

1. The horse ran.

_____

2. I ate lunch.

_____

J. Underline the prepositional phrases in each sentence. The number in parentheses tells you how many there are.

1. Nana told us to get off the couch and do something outside in the nice sunshine. (2)

2. By sheer bad luck, our display poster fell onto my head twice during our presentation. (3)

3. In a few weeks, we will be skiing along the ski trails of Jasper, Alberta. (3)

K. For each sentence, underline the word in parentheses that results in avoiding a double negative.

1. I can't see (anything / nothing) through this thick fog.

2. I haven't made (no / any) progress with my plan for eating healthier snacks.

3. You can leave your backpacks here; they won't go (nowhere / anywhere).

L. Write a descriptive paragraph about the most beautiful thing you have ever seen in nature. Give an accurate, sensory description by choosing effective adverbs and adjectives. Include prepositional phrases and interjections.

_____

_____

_____

_____

_____

_____

_____

_____

_____

_____

_____

M. Write a persuasive paragraph urging a friend from another place to visit the area where you live. Include coordinating conjunctions and subordinating conjunctions.

_____

_____

_____

_____

_____

_____

_____

_____

_____

_____

_____

_____

_____

CRAFT AND COMPOSE

Like math, writing has rules that need to be followed in a logical way. Like painting, writing also has methods that can be used to create different effects in a creative way.

Good writers craft each word, sentence, paragraph, or line of poetry with an art that makes their readers want to read more. This doesn't happen by accident: it comes from thinking about *what* you want to write, *why*, and for *whom*—and then *how*. Once you identify your topic, purpose, and audience, you can make the right decisions about how to grab your readers and get your message across to them clearly.

In this section, you will learn how your choices as a writer can make your writing lively and powerful.

"Any writer will be happy and good only if they know what they're doing and why they're doing it."

— Yann Martel

USE YOUR KNOWLEDGE: CHOOSING A TOPIC

When **choosing a topic** for a descriptive text, think about the people, events, and interests in your life that you know a lot about or that you feel strongly about.

Tapping into your own knowledge helps you write vivid, colourful, and detailed descriptions in order to make your topic come alive for your readers. For example, a person who lives in British Columbia is better able to describe the experience, sights, and sounds of living in that province than someone who lives in Ontario. When writing a descriptive text, use descriptive words to paint a picture unique to your experience!

Choosing a topic or an idea that interests you or that you feel strongly about can make the task of writing easy and enjoyable.

A. **Think of a topic for each category. Write some details, in point form, about the topic.**

1. place I have visited: _____

Details: _____

_____

2. current event I feel strongly about: _____

Details: _____

_____

3. person I admire: _____

Details: _____

_____

B. **Choose one of the topics from Exercise A and write a short paragraph about it.**

_____

_____

_____

_____

_____

_____

_____

_____

C. Write two descriptive paragraphs. Choose a topic that you know or care about, such as your favourite memory, a special person, or an important event. Use strong, descriptive words to help your readers picture your topic.

_____

_____

_____

_____

_____

_____

_____

_____

_____

_____

_____

_____

_____

_____

_____

_____

_____

_____

_____

_____

_____

_____

_____

_____

_____

_____

_____

_____

_____

CONSIDER PURPOSE AND AUDIENCE

When you write, it is important to think about your **purpose** and **audience**.

Your purpose is your reason for writing. It might be to explain, to entertain, to persuade, or to describe a topic. To decide, ask yourself, "Why do I want my audience to know about this topic?"

Your audience is any person or group who will read your work. Before writing, consider your audience's background knowledge of your topic. This will help you decide what details to include in your writing.

If, for example, your topic was about a favourite place and your audience was unfamiliar with this place, you would likely decide to describe it, using sensory details to help your audience picture the place in their minds.

> For example: My favourite place is under the shade of the tall pine tree at our cottage, overlooking the long, lazy river, on a hot August day.

A. **Read the topics and audiences described below. Decide on a purpose in each case and write it on the line provided. Then, underline the details that would be of interest to the audience based on their background knowledge. Write your reasons on the lines provided.**

1. **Topic:** a fall fair   **Audience:** out-of-town visitors who have never been to the fair

Purpose: _____

Details: a) the amount of money the fair brings to the town and its businesses

b) things to experience at the fair, such as rides, games, shows, and food

Reason: _____

_____

2. **Topic:** a movie review   **Audience:** people who want to see the movie

Purpose: _____

Details: a) your opinion of the movie, and whether or not you recommend it

b) unexpected plot twists and spoilers about how the movie ends

Reason: _____

_____

B. **Choose one of the topics from Exercise A and write a descriptive paragraph about it. Keep your purpose and your audience's background knowledge in mind.**

FORMULATE A THESIS: TOPIC VERSUS THESIS

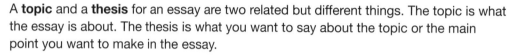

A **topic** and a **thesis** for an essay are two related but different things. The topic is what the essay is about. The thesis is what you want to say about the topic or the main point you want to make in the essay.

A thesis should not simply be a fact. It should identify your topic as well as your viewpoint on the topic. It answers the question "What is the purpose of my essay?"
For example: Topic—downhill skiing
Thesis—Downhill skiing is the most exciting winter sport.

In the example thesis, the author identifies the topic (downhill skiing) and presents a viewpoint (it is the most exciting winter sport).

A. Read each paragraph. From the two theses provided, choose the one that you think best states the purpose of the essay. Underline your choice.

1. Topic: winter camping

Everyone should go winter camping. It may sound cold and miserable, but it's not! Sleeping in weather so cold I can see my breath makes me appreciate the luxuries I have in life. Spending the day snowshoeing through dense woods, spying deer, red foxes, and different kinds of birds, makes me feel closer to nature. And, there is nothing so relaxing as sitting by a campfire at night soaking in its warmth, sipping on hot chocolate, and watching the reflection of the flames bounce off the white snow.

a) Winter camping is an unforgettable experience.   **b)** Winter camping is cold.

2. Topic: Canada Day

Celebrating Canada Day is a way of showing pride for your country. There are always lots of people out on the streets on Canada Day. Many of them paint their faces red and white and wave Canadian flags. The best part of Canada Day is watching the fireworks. They light up the sky in all different shapes and colours.

a) Fireworks are important to me.   **b)** Canada Day celebrations are important to me.

B. Write a thesis for this topic. Your thesis should identify your topic and your viewpoint.

Topic: last day of school

_____

_____

_____

_____

CREATE A SENSES CHART: ORGANIZING IDEAS

When you write, it is helpful to **organize your ideas**. One way to do so is to create a senses chart using the five senses: sight, sound, touch, taste, and smell.

For example: Topic—a day at the beach

See	Hear	Feel	Taste	Smell
• swimmers • boats	• children laughing • waves crashing	• hot sand • cool breeze	• hot dogs • chocolate ice cream	• sunscreen • salty water

In this example, the writer created a senses chart before writing about a day at the beach. This method of organization is particularly helpful when writing descriptive texts because sensory details make texts more interesting. These details will help the writer make the experience of being at the beach come alive for readers.

A. **The details below describe a day at a baseball game. Write the sense that each detail is related to on the line beside it.**

1. cheering _____

2. hot dogs _____

3. warm sun _____

4. fresh-cut grass _____

5. cool breeze _____

6. popcorn _____

7. sea of people _____

8. music _____

B. **Choose one of the following topics (or one of your own) and write it on the line below: auditioning for a play, warming up for a race, camping. Then, create a senses chart for the topic you chose. Try to include at least three details for each sense.**

Topic: _____

See	Hear	Feel	Taste	Smell

C. **Write a descriptive paragraph about the topic you chose in Exercise B. Use the details in your senses chart to make the experience come alive for your readers.**

LESSON 76

WRITE WHAT AND WHY: STRONG OPENINGS

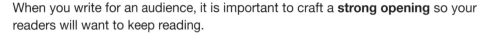

When you write for an audience, it is important to craft a **strong opening** so your readers will want to keep reading.

An essay should open with a thesis that identifies its main point. A good way to begin a descriptive essay is to identify the person, place, or thing that is being described. Then, reveal your viewpoint of it or why it is important to you.

For example: Where can you walk among the dinosaurs, tour the depths of the ocean, and visit ancient Greece? A museum. Museums are valuable because they bring interesting ideas to life and let you explore the past.

In the example, the topic of this descriptive essay is museums. The writer's viewpoint is that museums are valuable. The rest of the descriptive essay will support this viewpoint with sensory details.

A. **Write a strong opening for the descriptive paragraph below. Remember to include what the writer is writing about and why.**

_____

_____

Imagine you are listening to your favourite song in the whole world. Now, imagine you are listening to that song performed live at an outdoor concert on a beautiful summer day. You can feel the summer breeze on your face. The sound of the live music fills the open air and echoes all around you. People in the crowd are dancing and enjoying the music. It is a much more memorable experience than sitting alone in your room with your headphones on.

B. **Write a strong opening for each topic. Include what you want to write about and why.**

1. Topic: a relaxing place

Strong opening: _____

_____

2. Topic: a happy memory

Strong opening: _____

_____

C. **Write at least two paragraphs for an essay about one of the two topics in Exercise B. Begin your essay with the opening you wrote.**

FIND STRENGTHS AND WEAKNESSES: WRITING DETAILS

Writers use descriptive **details** about character and setting to make a story come alive for readers.

One way to add detail to your writing and depth to your characters is to determine your characters' strengths and weaknesses. This allows you to write about your characters as if they were real people. It also helps your readers relate to your characters, as they might share some of a character's strengths or weaknesses—or know someone who does.

To create a lifelike character, make a list of the character's strengths and weaknesses. Then, use these details in your writing. Sometimes, a strength can be related to a weakness.

For example: Penny's Strengths: funny, honest

Penny's Weaknesses: takes jokes too far; offends people with her honesty

As Penny laughed, she noticed that Jordan wasn't smiling. He frowned and walked away. She wondered what was wrong. All she had done was make a little joke about his new haircut.

A. Read each paragraph. From each list of strengths and weaknesses provided, underline the two most appropriate words that the writer likely had in mind when developing that character.

1. Ashish looked out at the faces in the audience. Everyone was staring at him, waiting. Ashish worried he wasn't good enough, and he could feel beads of sweat forming on his forehead. He remembered the words of his older sister: "Pretend that nobody's there; focus on your character." He closed his eyes and imagined being someone else. He opened his mouth to say his lines. At first, his voice was shaky. After a while, the words flowed confidently. He became absorbed in the scene and completely forgot that everyone else was there. At the end of the play, Ashish got a standing ovation.

   Ashish's strengths: funny   determined   loyal   generous   creative

   Ashish's weaknesses: nervous   angry   lazy   spiteful   insecure

2. The day of the test, Autumn's friends were nervous. They had been up late studying, and they spent their lunch break going over their notes. "Do you want me to quiz you?" Caitlin asked Autumn. "Pssh, no," she said. "I'm not worried; science is my best subject." Autumn spent her lunch break playing soccer. Then it was time for the test. As she looked around, she saw her classmates sweating and fidgeting nervously, but she felt totally calm. Then she started reading the test. She realized that she didn't know any of the answers! All of a sudden, she started to sweat. She found herself fidgeting nervously, just like her friends.

   Autumn's strengths: smart   calm   curious   confident   trustworthy

   Autumn's weaknesses: proud   polite   shy   presumptuous   lazy

B. **Create a character for a story. Make a list of three strengths and three weaknesses the character has.**

Character's name: _____

Strengths

1. _____

2. _____

3. _____

Weaknesses

1. _____

2. _____

3. _____

C. **Write a scene featuring the character you created in Exercise B. Make the character come alive for your readers by describing events that show both the character's strengths and weaknesses.**

_____

_____

_____

_____

_____

_____

_____

_____

_____

_____

_____

_____

_____

_____

_____

_____

_____

_____

USE YOUR SENSES: SUPPORTING DETAILS

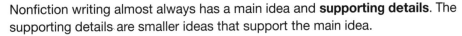

Nonfiction writing almost always has a main idea and **supporting details**. The supporting details are smaller ideas that support the main idea.

To write supporting details for a descriptive essay, use your senses. Sensory information includes sights, sounds, textures, tastes, and smells, and can help readers visualize and understand the main idea.

For example: The old house at the end of the street is straight out of a horror movie. (main idea)
The wood is rotten and all the windows are smashed. On windy days, the house creaks and a weird odour wafts out of it. (supporting details)

In this example, the author uses sensory information to write details that support the main idea.

A. Choose the sensory details that best support each main idea.

1. Main idea: The movie theatre on Main Street is always a mess.

a) The floors are sticky, and it always smells like stale popcorn and mildew.

b) I don't think the washrooms are cleaned very often.

2. Main idea: Riverside Park is a great place to visit in the summer.

a) The park is full of towering oak trees, and people fish along the river that flows through it.

b) The park is popular with tourists; quite a few visit every summer.

3. Main idea: My last visit to the dentist was horrible.

a) The taste of fluoride made me sick, and my mouth was open for so long it ached.

b) I always get a new toothbrush at the end of my visit, but I didn't get one that time.

B. Think about a place that inspires you. Write two sensory details that describe it.

Main idea: I think _____ is an inspirational place.

1. _____

_____

2. _____

_____

C. Write at least two descriptive paragraphs about the inspirational place you chose for Exercise B. Use the two sensory details you wrote and also add more sensory information to help readers visualize and understand the place.

ORDER BY TIME: ARRANGING DETAILS

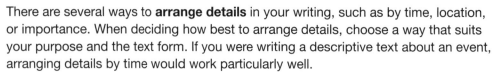

There are several ways to **arrange details** in your writing, such as by time, location, or importance. When deciding how best to arrange details, choose a way that suits your purpose and the text form. If you were writing a descriptive text about an event, arranging details by time would work particularly well.

For example: First, we made our way through the crowd of people. I could feel elbows knocking into me as we pushed our way to the front. We got a spot right in front of the stage. As we waited, we could feel the excitement growing in the crowd. People were hooting and chanting the band's name. Finally, the lights went out. The crowd went silent. Suddenly, a single note rang out.

Words that show time include *first, second, third, next, meanwhile, on (date), today, tomorrow, yesterday, suddenly, soon, finally, at last, now, later, before, after, while,* and *then.*

A. **The sentences below provide details about a past event, but they are in the wrong order. Show the correct order by writing a number on the line at the end of each sentence. Use time as your organizer.**

1. Then, I thought I heard some rustling coming from behind the couch. ___

2. As I walked in the room, the first thing I noticed was how clean it was. ___

3. Suddenly, all my friends and family jumped out from their hiding spots and shouted, "Surprise!" ___

4. I couldn't believe it; I thought everyone had forgotten my birthday! ___

5. Everything was tidy and organized—I hadn't seen our living room that clean in years. ___

B. **Write a short descriptive paragraph about a celebration you attended, such as a party, a wedding, or a graduation ceremony. Organize the details according to time.**

_____

_____

_____

_____

_____

C. **Underline the words in Exercise B that signal time to the readers. Reread the paragraph without these words. Think about how using time to arrange details helps readers visualize an event.**

SHOW CHARACTER AND SITUATION: WRITING DIALOGUE

Writers use **dialogue** for many reasons, including to show a character's traits, to express a character's feelings or mood, and to reveal information about a character's situation. Often, well-written dialogue can involve readers more effectively in a story than descriptive sentences or paragraphs.

For example: Robert whispered to Anna that he felt embarrassed. He started to blush.

"Ugh, I'm so embarrassed," Robert whispered to Anna, as he blushed hotly.

In the first example, the writer explains Robert's situation. The second example conveys the same information but uses dialogue to engage readers.

A. Read the dialogue. Underline the word in each list that best describes each character.

Ben: confident funny nervous   Mr. Ng: bashful concerned terrified

"Have a seat," said Mr. Ng. "Do you know why I wanted to talk to you?"

"I …. I don't know." Ben stammered. "Um …. No, I'm not sure."

"Ben, it's about your history test. It's not like you to fail. You're usually one of the top students. What happened? Did you study?"

"Yes. I mean, a little. I just sort of … ran out of time."

B. Revise the paragraph. Add dialogue to reveal information to your readers about each character's traits, feelings, mood, and situation.

The Changs had been driving all day. Jin and Mei were squished in the back seat. Jin was hungry and wanted to stop for ice cream. Mei just wanted to get home as fast as possible.

_____

_____

_____

_____

_____

_____

_____

_____

C. Write a story. Use dialogue to engage your readers. What can you reveal about your characters and their situations through dialogue?

_____

_____

_____

_____

_____

_____

_____

_____

_____

_____

_____

_____

_____

_____

_____

_____

_____

_____

_____

_____

_____

_____

_____

_____

_____

LESSON 81

MAKE LANGUAGE PRECISE: SENSORY WORDS

When writers use words that are vague or overused, their writing can be dull. Using precise language makes writing more interesting and vivid.

One way to make language precise is to use **sensory words**. This means that instead of using worn out, one-word descriptions, writers draw on their senses to describe a person, place, thing, event, or experience. They choose sensory words that make readers experience or visualize what is being described.

For example: The bus was *crowded*. (vague one-word description)

A *clamour of voices* filled my ears as I *pushed* my way past *outstretched arms* and *discarded backpacks* to the *only vacant seat* at the *back* of the bus. (precise sensory words)

A. **Rewrite each sentence by replacing the vague words with sensory words. Choose words to help readers see, hear, feel, taste, and/or smell what you are describing.**

1. It was hot outside.

_____

_____

2. It was windy on the sailboat.

_____

_____

3. The garbage dump smelled bad.

_____

_____

B. **Write a short paragraph describing a person, place, thing, event, or experience. Use sensory words to help your readers visualize what you are describing.**

_____

_____

_____

_____

_____

RESTATE WHAT AND WHY: STRONG CONCLUSIONS

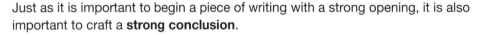

Just as it is important to begin a piece of writing with a strong opening, it is also important to craft a **strong conclusion**.

A conclusion for a descriptive essay should restate the *what* and *why* that you wrote about in the opening of your essay. It should remind readers of your essay's topic (*what*) and your viewpoint (*why*).

For example: Even though wind turbines create noise and are unattractive to some, they are still a worthwhile energy resource. The amount of green energy created by wind turbines is more beneficial than harmful.

In this example, the writer restates the essay's *what* (wind turbines are beneficial) and the *why* (the amount of green energy they create) in the conclusion. This leaves readers with a powerful message to think about.

A. Read each conclusion below. Write the *what* and *why* each conclusion restates.

1. Sometimes, you need to take a closer look at art to experience its true meaning. When I first looked at Paul-Emile Borduas's painting *Delicate Rustlings*, I just saw a bunch of random shapes. As I studied it closely, I noticed the intricate details and texture of the work.

What: _____

Why: _____

2. I used to think volunteering was a lot of hard work with no reward. My experience with volunteering at an animal shelter left me with a different perspective. Now, I regard volunteering as a way to learn new skills and enjoy the feeling of helping others.

What: _____

Why: _____

B. Write a strong conclusion for the descriptive text.

Our kitchen is my favourite room in the house. It holds our lives together. My dad does most of the cooking, and the aromas he creates beckon us to meals in the morning and evening. I refer to the table in our kitchen as "homework central." It is there that my sister and I meet, spread out our books, and finish up our work. Surrounded by blue-green walls and lit by soft overhead lights, the kitchen reminds me of an oasis; it is the one place where everyone in our family gathers to work, to eat, and to share our lives.

_____

_____

_____

C. Write two descriptive paragraphs about an image that you found memorable. Open your first paragraph by stating what you are writing about and why. End with a strong conclusion that restates the *what* and *why*.

CATCH YOUR READERS' ATTENTION: EFFECTIVE TITLES

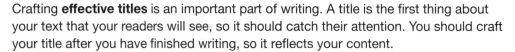

Crafting **effective titles** is an important part of writing. A title is the first thing about your text that your readers will see, so it should catch their attention. You should craft your title after you have finished writing, so it reflects your content.

An effective title for a descriptive text gives a unique description of the topic. It should also catch readers' attention and make them want to keep reading.

For example: My Day at the Skate Park ✗
Sun, Ramps, and Rails ✓
My Favourite Meal ✗
Dim Sum for Dinner ✓

It is important to format a title correctly. Capitalize the first and last word in your title and every word in between except articles (*a, an*, and *the*), prepositions (such as *of, at, to, in*, and *about*), and conjunctions (such as *and, but*, and *or*).

A. Write an effective title for each topic.

1. Topic: eating lunch with my friends

_____

2. Topic: the funniest person I know

_____

3. Topic: what makes me special

_____

4. Topic: my favourite out-of-school activity

_____

B. Write a brief descriptive paragraph about your favourite food. Then, create an effective title for your paragraph.

Title: _____

_____

_____

_____

_____

_____

_____

IMPROVE WORD CHOICE AND SPELLING: REVISING

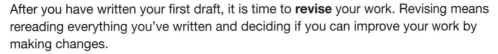

After you have written your first draft, it is time to **revise** your work. Revising means rereading everything you've written and deciding if you can improve your work by making changes.

First, check your choice of words. Doing this is especially important with descriptive writing. Choose strong words to describe your topic and convey your point. Replace vague or overused adjectives, nouns, or verbs with specific ones.

For example: Fiona *took* her diary out of her sister's hands.
Fiona *snatched* her diary out of her sister's hands.

Also, check your writing for any missing information. You can improve clarity by adding details.

For example: It was raining outside. Then we made a run for it.
It was pouring outside. We put on our raincoats and made a run for the car.

Finally, make sure your writing is clear and precise and your spelling is correct.

Revising and editing your work is an important part of the writing process. To help you check if your writing is smooth and free of errors, try reading it aloud. You can often hear errors before you see them.

A. **There are two spelling errors in each sentence. Underline the errors and write the correct spellings.**

1. It was pouring rane when they made the long walk back to they're car.

_____   _____

2. I felt a rush of exitement as soon as I jumped off the diving bored and plunged into the water.

_____   _____

3. Suddenly, a surge of pane shot through my ankle as I kicked the socker ball.

_____   _____

4. The runer had to take a break to drink some water and catch her breathe.

_____   _____

B. **Replace the underlined word in each sentences with a more specific adjective, noun, or verb.**

1. The runner <u>went</u> across the finish line and cheered triumphantly. _____

2. It was a <u>nice</u> day at the beach. _____

3. The neighbour's <u>pet</u> ran into a skunk and got sprayed. _____

4. The trees were <u>moving</u> wildly just before the storm hit. _____

C. **Improve the clarity of each sentence by adding missing information or more detail.**

1. Isaac and Michael went home early because he was feeling sick.

_____

_____

2. The man walks his dog every day, even when the weather is bad.

_____

_____

3. We had to turn around because I left my bag.

_____

_____

D. **Write a paragraph describing the best gift you have ever received. Read over your descriptive paragraph, checking for spelling errors, word choice, and clarity.**

_____

_____

_____

_____

_____

_____

_____

_____

_____

_____

_____

_____

_____

_____

_____

_____

_____

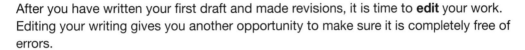

CORRECT SENTENCES: EDITING

After you have written your first draft and made revisions, it is time to **edit** your work. Editing your writing gives you another opportunity to make sure it is completely free of errors.

The types of errors to watch for and fix include sentence fragments and run-on sentences. A sentence fragment is a group of words that does not express a complete thought because it is missing a noun or a verb. A run-on sentence is two sentences joined together without the correct punctuation or connecting word.

For example: Falling from the sky. ✗ (fragment)

Large drops of rain were falling from the sky. ✓

She was almost at the finish line her heart was pounding. ✗ (run-on)

She was almost at the finish line. *Her* heart was pounding. ✓

She was almost at the finish line, *and* her heart was pounding. ✓

Editing your work is an important part of the writing process. To help you spot errors in your writing, try reading it aloud. You can often hear errors before you see them.

A. **Correct these run-on sentences and sentence fragments.**

1. The wind turbines made a lot of noise many local residents complained.

_____

_____

2. Stared at the painting for over ten minutes.

_____

_____

3. Hidden at the bottom of my backpack under all the school books.

_____

_____

4. They dug up the front yard to put in a vegetable garden it was hard work.

_____

_____

5. The dark clouds were moving closer to the baseball field the team kept playing.

_____

_____

B. **Check for sentence fragments and run-on sentences in the following paragraph. Rewrite the paragraph, correcting any errors you find.**

Running a 5 km race is hard work, but the feeling of accomplishment makes it worth it. I had been training for months I knew I was ready. On the day of the race, I was nervous. Looking at the other runners. They looked so strong and confident. I imagined them racing past me as I huffed and puffed in last place. When the race started, all those thoughts disappeared. Focused on my breathing, on keeping a steady pace, and on finishing the race.

_____

_____

_____

_____

_____

_____

_____

_____

_____

_____

C. **Write a descriptive paragraph about a person, place, or event that is special to you. Check your work for run-on sentences and sentence fragments. Fix any errors you find.**

_____

_____

_____

_____

_____

_____

_____

_____

_____

_____

_____

_____

_____

SECTION REVIEW

A. Write a sentence describing a topic for each writing idea below.

1. something I want to change in my community

_____

_____

2. a person who has taught me a lot

_____

_____

B. Read the topic and audience described below. Decide on a purpose for writing and two details that would be of interest to the audience given their background knowledge.

Topic: after-school activities   Audience: classmates who recently moved to your school

Purpose: _____

Details: 1. _____

2. _____

C. Write a thesis for the following topic.

Topic: a true friend

Thesis: _____

_____

D. Choose one of the topics listed below. Create a senses chart for the topic. Include at least two details for each sense.

playing a sport   visiting relatives   going on a trip

Topic: _____

See	Hear	Feel	Taste	Smell

E. Write a strong opening for each of the topics.

  1. Topic: a big surprise

   Opening: _____

   _____

  2. Topic: senior citizens

   Opening: _____

   _____

F. Read the following paragraph. Then, underline two strengths from the list that describe Jesse's character.

Jesse had been waiting in line for hours. The book signing was supposed to have started ten minutes ago, but the author was late. It was cold and rainy, and Jesse was getting soaked. Then, someone put a sign on the door. "They're letting us in!" thought Jesse. But the sign said *Book signing delayed 30 minutes*. "Thirty minutes?" sighed Jesse. He couldn't wait a minute longer! As he was about to leave, Jesse remembered his friend Marwan, who was at home with a broken leg. This was Marwan's favourite author, and Jesse had promised to get an autographed book for him. Reluctantly, Jesse kept his place in line.

Jesse's strengths: **1.** patient   **2.** funny   **3.** reliable   **4.** compassionate

G. The events described below are in the wrong order. Correct the order by writing a number on the line at the end of each sentence; use time as your organizer. Underline all the words in the sentences that show time.

  1. "Thank you for coming," she said. "Let's begin. We're here to discuss the transit proposal." ____

  2. When we got to the Town Hall, the room was packed. We found a place to stand at the back. ____

  3. Then, the councillor stepped up to the podium and signalled for everyone's attention. ____

  4. Soon the room was in an uproar and everyone was speaking at once. ____

H. Rewrite the sentence by replacing the underlined, overused word with vivid, sensory words.

They live in a <u>beautiful</u> house.

_____

I. Read the run-on sentence and sentence fragment below. Rewrite them as complete sentences.

  1. My grandmother likes flowers she works in her garden every day.

   _____

   _____

  2. Soared over the trees and flew away.

   _____

   _____

J. **Write a descriptive paragraph about a Canadian landmark. Include an opening and a conclusion that tells your readers what you are writing about, and why. Create a title for your piece that will capture your readers' interest.**

Title: _____

_____

_____

_____

_____

_____

_____

_____

_____

_____

_____

K. **Write a short conversation about a conflict between two strangers that had a peaceful resolution. Use dialogue to show each character's traits or feelings and to reveal information about the situation.**

_____

_____

_____

_____

_____

_____

_____

_____

_____

_____

_____

DEVELOP RESEARCH SKILLS

Research is not just what you do to find an answer; it is an essential part of learning and an important part of the writing process.

The methods you use for your research will affect the quality of the information you get, whether you are looking up data to help you understand an issue or searching for photos to help you illustrate a point. Good information makes good writing.

In this section, you will learn about the skills that make an effective researcher.

"The constant happiness is curiosity."

— Alice Munro

THINK CRITICALLY: INQUIRY QUESTIONS

Inquiry questions help you to interpret information, identify patterns and trends, and encourage critical thinking. An effective inquiry question is ...

- *meaningful*—Choose a topic that interests you.
- *open-ended*—There should be no simple answer; in fact, there may be several parts to the answer.
- *debatable*—Consider an inquiry question that people may have different opinions about.
- *answered by research*—You will need to use classroom, library, and online resources to find an answer.
- *focused*—Be specific, because questions that are too general can be difficult to manage.

For example: How are the rights and freedoms of Canadians today linked to the struggles of people in 1914?

A. **Consider each of the following inquiry questions. On the line beside each question, write "Effective" or "Ineffective." Explain your choice.**

1. How do you make pancakes? _____

_____

_____

2. What are the five most important traits of a globally responsible nation? _____

_____

_____

B. **Read the following inquiry question. Explain whether it is effective or not, and revise it if necessary.**

What percentage of Earth's surface is covered in fresh water?

_____

_____

_____

_____

_____

_____

_____

FIND SYNONYMS AND ANTONYMS: RESEARCHING WORDS

Researching words like synonyms and antonyms can help you find the perfect word for your writing. A synonym is a word that means the same or almost the same thing as another word. An antonym is a word that means the opposite or almost the opposite of another word.

Use a print or online thesaurus to research synonyms and antonyms. Most thesauruses will list a few synonyms and antonyms for each word they include.

    For example: happy

               synonyms: contented, delighted, cheerful

               antonyms: unhappy, miserable, morose, furious

To decide which synonym or antonym to use, think about the context it will be used in.

    For example: Alicia's parents were *not happy* when she was late.

Instead of focusing on what Alicia's parents were *not*, choose an appropriate antonym for the word *happy* that best describes how Alicia's parents actually felt.

    For example: Alicia's parents were *furious* when she was late.

A. **Underline two synonyms for each bolded word. Use a thesaurus to help you.**

1. **alleviate**	intensify	reduce	aggravate	diminish
2. **accomplice**	adversary	abettor	opponent	collaborator
3. **paucity**	deficiency	scarcity	plethora	abundance
4. **sprightly**	lively	doddering	active	lethargic

B. **Complete each sentence by writing an antonym for the underlined word. Use a thesaurus to find the best antonym.**

1. Attendance at the assembly is _____ rather than <u>voluntary</u>.

2. Do you believe the incident was <u>accidental</u> or _____?

3. The <u>horizontal</u> axis intersects at a 90° angle with the _____ axis.

4. The opposite of <u>war</u> is _____.

5. Is it better to be _____ or <u>strict</u>?

C. **Using a thesaurus, write the most formal and informal synonym and antonym you can find for the word *calm*.**

Formal synonym: _____   Informal synonym: _____

Formal antonym: _____   Informal antonym: _____

D. **Review some of your writing and create a list of at least five words you use frequently. Use a thesaurus to find synonyms and antonyms for each word in your list.**

CHOOSE RESOURCES: LIBRARY RESEARCH

When you do **library research**, you have access to many reliable resources that will help you find information. Because these resources are usually professionally written and edited, they are more trustworthy than amateur websites.

Select print or online resources that are most likely to help you find the information you are looking for. Search the *library database* for books on specific topics. Use online resources (such as encyclopedias or news sites) to locate general information about specific topics. Look in a *newspaper* to find updates on current events. Search for maps and other geographical information in an *atlas* or online. Use a *manual* to help you discover how to do something or how something works.

A. **Read each scenario and write the appropriate resource for research. Then, answer the prompt that follows.**

1. Matthew has to write a report about the fur trade. He should use a/an _____ to help him find information because

_____

_____

2. Batya needs to figure out how fix his old bike. A/An _____ would be a good place for Batya to look because

_____

_____

3. Srijut is researching an earthquake that happened in Japan yesterday. Srijut will be more likely

to find the information in a/an _____ than in an encyclopedia because

_____

_____

B. **Read each of the following scenarios. State which resource(s) would be most helpful in finding the information needed.**

1. Axel is looking for information about the current heat wave. _____

2. Permina needs to find information about Cree beadwork. _____

3. Manny wants to find out how to reset the time on his alarm clock. _____

C. **Select a topic that interests you. What resources might help you prepare your report or presentation? Write a short list outlining your topic, the resources you would use, and how each resource might help you.**

CONDUCT ONLINE RESEARCH: KEYWORDS

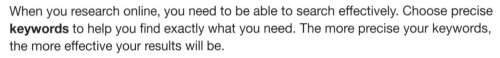

When you research online, you need to be able to search effectively. Choose precise **keywords** to help you find exactly what you need. The more precise your keywords, the more effective your results will be.

Consider your research purpose. What do you want to find out?

For example, suppose your topic is the Fenian Raids. To find out about the raids, try *Fenian Raids* as your keyword search.

To discover how they affected Confederation, try *Fenian Raids impact Confederation Canada*.

Use your topic and purpose to help you choose the most important keywords. Use nouns whenever possible. Place the most important words first, and use as many words as needed to narrow your search.

Avoid using questions and sentences. Proper spelling is important, but punctuation and capitalization are not always necessary.

Look through the list of search results for the best match and for reliable sources, such as online encyclopedias or educational websites. If necessary, refine your keywords to yield better matches.

A. **Which keyword search would be most effective for researching the environmental impact of an oil spill that happened off the coast of California on May 19, 2015?**

   a) oil spill

   b) California oil spill 2015

   c) California oil spill may 19 2015 impact

   d) impact oil spill 2015

B. **Read each question. Write effective keywords that will lead you to information to help answer the question.**

   1. What organizations in Yellowknife offer CPR courses?

   _____

   2. What is the focus of the Water for People organization?

   _____

   3. Does the media help or hinder teens' understanding of healthy eating?

   _____

C. **Write three questions you would like to find answers to. Below each question, write keywords that will help you find your answer(s).**

    1. Question: _____

      _____

      Keywords: _____

    2. Question: _____

      _____

      Keywords: _____

    3. Question: _____

      _____

      Keywords: _____

D. **For one question you wrote in Exercise C, enter your keywords into a search engine. Explore the matches that are provided. Write a short paragraph describing the overall effectiveness of your keyword searches.**

    _____

    _____

    _____

    _____

    _____

E. **Read the following keyword challenge. Divide the challenge into parts that you believe will best help you research the answer. Use effective keyword searches for each part. Below each keyword search, write any findings that may help you answer the challenge.**

On what day of the week did the first prime minister of Canada celebrate his tenth birthday?

    1. First keyword search: _____

      Findings: _____

      _____

    2. Second keyword search: _____

      Findings: _____

      _____

    3. Third keyword search (if needed): _____

      Findings: _____

      _____

Answer to keyword challenge:

_____

CONSIDER BIAS: PRIMARY AND SECONDARY SOURCES

When you look at primary and secondary sources of information, ensure that you think about bias.

A **primary source** is an account or object directly connected to an event, experience, or time period. A first-hand written description, an artifact, and a piece of art created by someone are all examples of primary sources.

A **secondary source** is an account of an event or experience by someone who was not present to directly experience the event, time, or place. Resources such as encyclopedias, nonfiction books, and newspaper articles are secondary sources.

Bias occurs when an author or creator of information favours one side over another, resulting in an unbalanced or one-sided account of an event. Both primary and secondary sources may contain bias. As you research, ask yourself whether all perspectives of an event have been taken into account.

A. Write a response to each question.

1. Why might some primary sources, such as diary entries or letters written by soldiers at war, contain bias?

_____

_____

_____

2. Why might secondary sources, such as history books about a war, contain bias?

_____

_____

_____

3. Why is it important to look for alternate perspectives, points of view, or attitudes when researching?

_____

_____

_____

B. Find a news report about a current event in print or online. Identify if the report is a primary or secondary source, or a mix of both. Ask yourself what perspective might be missing from the report. Write a paragraph about whether you believe the news report is biased toward one perspective.

SPOT HOAXES: ONLINE SOURCES

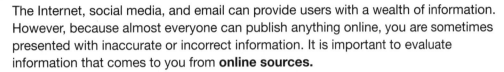

The Internet, social media, and email can provide users with a wealth of information. However, because almost everyone can publish anything online, you are sometimes presented with inaccurate or incorrect information. It is important to evaluate information that comes to you from **online sources.**

Examples of hoaxes include urban legends and misleading websites. Urban legends are stories that many people believe to be true, but that have been made up to entertain or to explain random events. Misleading websites purposely provide false information. Sometimes the false information is provided to deceive, but sometimes it is provided as comedy, parody, or entertainment, and the audience is expected to understand that the information is untrue.

To confirm whether something is a hoax, do further research. Research some of the claims made within the text. Find additional sources and determine whether they support or contradict the information. Use a site dedicated to tracking online hoaxes.

A. **You have just read a website article that says your new phone can be fully charged by putting it in the microwave on high power for two minutes. What should you do?**

a) Immediately assume that this is a hoax and ignore it.

b) Do further research to determine whether this is legitimate or not.

c) Test this out in the microwave when your phone needs charging.

B. **Explain your choice for Exercise A.**

_____

_____

C. **Read each website title. Explain why each site might be a hoax and how you could check it.**

1. Shed 20 Pounds in ONE WEEK with Banana Peel Vitamins

_____

_____

2. Saskatchewan's Sticky Note Crop at Risk

_____

_____

D. **Make a list of clues that can help you spot an online hoax.**

INVESTIGATE COPYRIGHT: PLAGIARISM

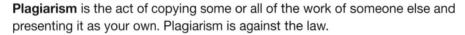

Plagiarism is the act of copying some or all of the work of someone else and presenting it as your own. Plagiarism is against the law.

Copyright is the law that protects people from having their work stolen. Text, photos, images, music, videos, and all other creative works are protected by copyright law.

This means that you can't copy and paste creative work into reports or presentations without crediting the creator. You may take notes from a source, as long as you rewrite them in your own words and credit the author.

Investigate the copyright status of any resources you want to use for schoolwork or other purposes. Be especially careful if you're posting your work online. With most copyright materials, you must determine who created the work, ask permission to use it, pay to use it if necessary, and credit the creator before sharing your project online.

Many online materials have Creative Commons copyright licences. These licences give specific instructions for how the creator of the work is willing to share his or her work. To find these sources in your research, add "Creative Commons" to your keyword search.

A. Read the following statements. Write "True" or "False" on the lines provided.

    1. It's always OK to include a song in a video you share online as long as you credit the songwriter. _____

    2. If you wish to use a Creative Commons photo in your report, you must first read over the licence to make sure you follow the instructions outlined by the photographer. _____

    3. It is acceptable to copy sentences from sources and write them word for word in your report, without using quotation marks, as long as you credit the source. _____

B. In your own words, define the following terms:

    1. copyright

    _____

    2. plagiarism

    _____

    3. Creative Commons

    _____

C. Find three creative works online that have Creative Commons licences and click on the CC icon of each one. View the details for using each work. Write a paragraph explaining your finding.

IN-TEXT CITATIONS: CITING RESEARCH

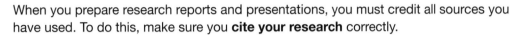

When you prepare research reports and presentations, you must credit all sources you have used. To do this, make sure you **cite your research** correctly.

You can cite your research at the end of your report, on a works cited or bibliography page. You can also use in-text citations with direct quotes or paraphrased ideas.

To create an in-text citation for a print source, include within the text of your report the author's name and the page number of the source. The author's name may either appear within parentheses following the information or within the sentence itself. The page number must appear in parentheses after the information.

For example: Most animal mouths have adapted over time (Hickman 56).
Hickman explains that most animal mouths have adapted over time based on the type of food each animal eats (56).

For web sources without page numbers, include the author's name (if known) or the website title. For each source you mention in an in-text citation, provide a complete citation in your bibliography or works cited page.

A. **Read the following statement. Write "True" or "False" and explain your choice.**

It is acceptable to write a report and list your sources only in a bibliography or works cited page, without crediting sources in the body of your report. _____

_____

_____

_____

B. **Rewrite the information below using your own words. Include an in-text citation in your rewrite.**

Author: Katrina Potter   Page: 82

Nonverbal communication is any communication not involving words. Examples include body language such as facial expressions, posture, spatial distance between two people, and touch.

_____

_____

_____

C. **Find a print or online source related to a topic you are studying. In your own words, write a few sentences using information from the source. Include an in-text citation that credits the source.**

MAINTAIN A CITATIONS LIST: RESEARCH NOTES

When you prepare a report, presentation, or essay, you must credit all sources that you use. Keep track of sources as you write **research notes,** so you have the information ready when it is time to write your report.

Create a citations list to track both print and online sources. Each time you find a new source, create a citation for it and add it to your list. As you write notes, record the number of the citation for the source you are using beside your notes. For example, if your notes are from your third source, write "3" beside the notes. If your source has page numbers, include the page number where you found the information in your notes.

For print sources, include the title, author, publisher, date, and city of publication for each citation on your list.

For online sources, include the author (if known), title of the web page, title of the website, date the site was created or last updated, and date you visited the site. You might also want to bookmark each site in case you need to go back to one.

When you prepare your report, use your citations list to help you write your final bibliography or works cited page. Remember to format your final citations according to the style assigned by your teacher.

A. Respond to the following questions:

1. If the author of an online source is not known, what information about the source should you include on your citations list?

   _____

   _____

2. Maxime has kept a working citations list while doing research for her report. When Maxime begins to write her report, she is confused by some information in her notes. How can Maxime's citations list help her?

   _____

   _____

   _____

B. List three ways that keeping a working citations list can make the process of preparing a report or presentation easier. You can use point form.

_____

_____

_____

C. **Choose one of the inquiry questions below. Find three resources to help you answer your question. Write a few notes from each source, and keep track of your sources by keeping a working citations list.**

What efforts has my community put into place to become more sustainable?

How effective has international fundraising been in improving the quality of life of people living in Haiti?

_____

_____

_____

_____

_____

_____

_____

_____

_____

_____

_____

_____

_____

_____

_____

_____

_____

_____

_____

_____

_____

_____

D. **Think about the process you used to keep track of sources in Exercise C. What worked? What didn't work? Write a paragraph explaining a step-by-step plan for how you will track your sources in the future.**

CITE YOUR SOURCES: PARAPHRASING AND QUOTING

When you **paraphrase**, you use your own words to explain someone else's ideas.

When you **quote**, you use a person's exact words and indicate to whom the words belong.

All or almost all of your research paper should be in your own words. However, you may want to quote someone in specific circumstances, such as the following:

- to show that an expert supports your point of view
- to give a definition
- to use specific words as evidence (for example, when proving your thesis about a novel)
- when the meaning would be lost if stated in other words

When you quote or paraphrase, credit your source with an in-text citation so that it is clear where the information or quote came from. If the information comes from a print source, include the page number after your in-text citation.

For example: McNab defines virtual reality as "an artificial, 3-D environment made accessible by computers" (23).

Ensure that for every in-text citation, you create a full citation in your bibliography or works cited page.

A. Rewrite the following information in your own words.

1. In the Maritime colonies, shipbuilding was an important industry. Fishing and overseas trade were flourishing, and by the 1850s, carpenters, sailmakers, and woodturners in shipyards were building approximately 350 ships per year.

_____

_____

_____

2. While Canada's official languages are English and French, there are more than 60 Indigenous languages and more than 100 other languages spoken in this country.

_____

_____

B. When you paraphrase or quote information, why do you think it is important to credit your source both within the body of your report or presentation and in the bibliography or works cited page?

_____

_____

C. **Read the following paragraph about Hurricane Hazel. Identify the main idea and select one sentence or part of a sentence that you may wish to quote in a report. Write point-form notes focusing on key facts and details.**

On October 15 and 16, 1954, Hurricane Hazel struck Toronto and the surrounding region. Although Hazel struck the region as an extratropical storm, its power was equal to a Category 1 hurricane. The effects of the storm were devastating. Winds reached 124 kilometres per hour, over 200 millimetres of rain fell, and 81 people died. About 4000 families were left homeless due to raging floods. The total damages caused by the storm were estimated at $100 million (equivalent to about $1 billion today). Hurricane Hazel remains the most notorious hurricane in Canadian history, as well as Toronto's worst natural disaster.

_____

_____

_____

_____

_____

_____

D. **Use your notes to write a paragraph about Hurricane Hazel. Don't look at the original paragraph as you write. Remember to include the quote you chose. Assume that the paragraph is from page 122 of a book by Letitia Bronwell.**

_____

_____

_____

_____

_____

_____

_____

_____

_____

_____

_____

_____

_____

_____

_____

SECTION REVIEW

A. **Read each of the following inquiry questions. Circle *E* if you think it is effective and *I* if you think it is ineffective. Then, explain your choice.**

1. What strategies should be implemented to protect the world's supply of fresh water?   I   E

   _____

   _____

2. Who won the Nobel Peace Prize in 2015?   I   E

   _____

   _____

B. **Underline two synonyms for each bolded word. Use a thesaurus to help you.**

1. **diversity**   assortment   distraction   channel   variety

2. **despondency**   pestilence   response   pessimism   despair

3. **slanderous**   disparaging   defamatory   valiant   exhilarating

C. **Complete the following sentences by writing antonyms for the underlined words. Use a thesaurus to help you.**

1. I would much rather _____ than <u>hinder</u> your progress.

2. <u>Scatter</u> the seeds in the spring, _____ wildflowers in the summer.

3. While she was <u>boisterous</u>, he was more _____.

D. **When was the last time you used library or online resources to research? Write about the resources that you used. Include information about how effective each resource was.**

_____

_____

_____

_____

_____

_____

_____

_____

_____

E. **Read the following keyword challenge. Divide the challenge into parts to help you research the answer. Create an effective keyword search for each part. Record the keywords you used and any useful findings. Then, answer the challenge.**

What city is the birthplace of the Canadian prime minister who was in office when Canada's current flag was first raised on Parliament Hill?

a) First keyword search: _____

Findings: _____

_____

b) Second keyword search: _____

Findings: _____

_____

Answer to keyword challenge: _____

F. **Why is it important to think about bias when you look at primary and secondary sources?**

_____

_____

_____

G. **Read each website title. Explain why the site might be a hoax.**

1. T-Rex Egg Hatches at Archeological Site

_____

_____

2. Roasted Sun-Dried Ice Cream

_____

_____

H. **Complete the following statements to show how to follow copyright law and avoid plagiarism.**

1. If you wish to use a Creative Commons photo in your report, you must _____

_____

_____

2. When taking notes from a book or website, you must _____

_____

_____

I. **Read the following paragraph about the Bay of Fundy. Identify the main idea and select part of a sentence that you might wish to quote in a report. Write point-form notes focusing on key facts and details.**

The Bay of Fundy is located in Atlantic Canada between New Brunswick and Nova Scotia. This ocean bay is famous for having the highest tides in the world. Every day, approximately 160 billion tonnes of water flows into and out of the Bay, resulting in tides that rise and fall over 15 metres. In some places, the water gradually rises from low to high tide, whereas in others it flows in turbulent rapids. Because the tides regularly churn up the seabed, the seawater in the region is nutrient-rich. The nutrients attract a wide variety of marine life. Eight species of whale live in the area, including the rare Northern Right Whale. Popular activities in the Bay of Fundy include sightseeing, whitewater rafting, sea kayaking, boating, hiking, and whale watching.

Main idea: _____

Possible quote: _____

_____

Notes: _____

_____

_____

_____

_____

_____

_____

_____

J. **Assume the paragraph in Exercise I comes from page 78 of a book written by Donald Whettle. Use your notes to write a paragraph that paraphrases Whettle's ideas. Include the quote you selected. Use in-text citations to cite your source, using proper formatting.**

_____

_____

_____

_____

_____

_____

_____

_____

_____

_____

K. **Research a topic of interest, using at least two sources. Identify the main idea, and select one sentence or part of a sentence that you might wish to use as a quote. Write point-form notes in your own words, focusing on key facts and details. Create a citations list, and track your sources in the margin beside your quote and notes.**

Topic: _____

Possible quote: _____

_____

Notes: _____

_____

_____

_____

_____

_____

_____

_____

_____

L. **Use your point-form notes in Exercise K to write a short report in your own words. Include the quote you selected. Use in-text citations to cite your sources, using proper formatting. Record your citations list.**

_____

_____

_____

_____

_____

_____

_____

_____

_____

_____

_____

_____

_____

ANSWER KEY

Work with Vocabulary

Lesson 1—Use a Similar Word: Synonyms

A. Answers will vary. Write a synonym for each word in parentheses. *Sample answers*:

   1. commence, begin   **2.** endeavour   **3.** purchase

B. **1.** treaties   **2.** transfer   **3.** granted

C. Answers will vary.

D. Answers will vary.

Lesson 2—Use the Opposite Word: Antonyms

A. light, fluffy, weightless

B. Answers will vary. *Sample answers*:

   1. neutral, indifferent

   2. affordable, reasonable

   3. middle-aged, mature

C. Answers will vary.

D. Answers will vary.

Lesson 3—Choose the Correct Spelling: Homophones

A. **1.** write/right   **3.** won/one

   2. fourth/forth   **4.** meat/meet

B. **1.** sent   **2.** peace   **3.** they're; there

   Memory tricks will vary. *Sample answers*:

   1. If you are smelling something, it's scent not sent

   2. I want a piece of pie

   3. It's not over here but over there. If I can replace *they're* with *they are*, and the sentence still makes sense, then I've got the right homophone.

C. Answers will vary. Check that you have used each homophone correctly.

D. Answers will vary. Check that you have used each homophone correctly.

Lesson 4—Expand Your Vocabulary: Root Words

A. **1.** d   **2.** a   **3.** b   **4.** c

B. **1.** False   **2.** True   **3.** False

   Explanations will vary. *Sample answers*:

   1. The root word *photo* means "light," not "shape," so *photobiology* is the study of how different living things react to light.

2. The root word *manu* means "hand," so a manuscript is something written by hand.

3. The root word *form* means "shape," not "skill," so batter that *conforms* when poured into a pan takes the shape of the pan.

C. Answers will vary. *Sample answers*:

   1. manipulate, manufacture, manicure

   2. artisan, artificial, artistry

D. Answers will vary.

Lesson 5—Understand Word Beginnings: Prefixes

A. **1.** in   **3.** mis   **5.** il   **7.** ir   **9.** il

   2. ir   **4.** in   **6.** in   **8.** mis

B. **1.** misplaced   **3.** misspelled   **5.** irrelevant

   2. illegible   **4.** irresponsible

C. Answers will vary. Check your answers in a dictionary.

D. Answers will vary. Check your answers in a dictionary.

Lesson 6—Understand Word Endings: Suffixes

A. **1.** security   **3.** absorption   **5.** arrival

   2. entertainment   **4.** forgiveness   **6.** endurance

B. **1.** conductor   **3.** listener

   2. combination   **4.** attendance

C. **1.** confusion   **2.** confidence

   Sentences will vary.

D. Answers will vary.

Lesson 7—Combine Two Words: Contractions

A. **1.** I have   **3.** would have

   2. He has   **4.** How did

B. **1.** I should've made sure I had my water bottle before I left the house.

   2. Our team is winning, even though we've never played beach volleyball before!

   3. Sanjay asked, "Where'd Coach Ferguson go?"

   4. Rashid answered, "She's gone to talk to the referee."

C. **1.** might've   **2.** why'd

   Sentences will vary.

D. Answers will vary.

Lesson 8—Mind Your Meaning: Denotation and Connotation

A. **1.** C, D   **2.** D, C

B. Answers will vary.

Lesson 9—Be Clear and Interesting: Descriptive Words

A. Answers will vary. *Sample answers:*

  1. scurried   **2.** talented   **3.** tempestuous

B. Answers will vary. Rewrite each sentence, replacing each underlined word with a stronger word that fits the context.

C. Answers will vary. Replace each instance of the words *good* or *help* with a stronger word that fits the context.

D. Answers will vary.

Lesson 10—Use Slang: Informal and Formal Language

A. bromance—a close friendship between two males; chill—calm down and relax; frenemy—an enemy posing as a friend

B. **1.** double-double   **3.** zone out

  2. slacker   **4.** selfie

C. Answers will vary.

D. Answers will vary.

Lesson 11—Use Variety: Literary Devices

A. **1.** a   **2.** b

B. Answers will vary. *Sample answers:*

  1. simile; Fatima's hair was smooth and soft.

  2. idiom; Jared called my name as loudly as he could.

  3. onomatopoeia, alliteration; Theo's feet landed heavily on each stair, making loud noises.

  4. personification; The tree's heavy branches made a deep, creaking sound in the gusts of wind.

C. Answers will vary. *Sample answers:*

  Celeste spoke softly,
  "This old house creaks and cracks
  and has corners like night.
  My heart is a jackhammer."

D. Answers will vary.

Section Review

A. Answers will vary. *Sample answers*: **1.** chat; discussion **2.** awesome; delicious **3.** wrapped up; completed **4.** swap; exchange **5.** cozy; at ease

This exercise is a review for Lesson 1.

B. Answers will vary. *Sample answers*: yummy, delicious, delectable

This exercise is a review for Lesson 2.

C. **1.** here   **3.** compliment   **5.** piece

  2. board   **4.** weight

This exercise is a review for Lesson 3.

D. Answers will vary.

This exercise is a review for Lesson 4.

E. Answers will vary. *Sample answers*: illogical, entertainment/entertainer, misconduct/conductor, non-drowsy/drowsiness, perseverance

This exercise is a review for Lessons 5 and 6.

F. Answers will vary. *Sample answers*: Answer 1: No, I've never thought about what might've happened if we'd found creatures on the Moon. Answer 2: No, I have never thought about what might have happened if we had found creatures on the Moon.

This exercise is a review for Lesson 7.

G. Answers will vary. *Sample answers*: denotation: an insect; connotation: flits from person to person

This exercise is a review for Lesson 8.

H. **1.** idiom   **2.** metaphor   **3.** personification   **4.** simile

Explanations will vary. *Sample answers*:

  1. something that brings great joy or relief

  2. something or someone very outdated

  3. travelled a short distance as fast as possible

  4. incredibly slowly

This exercise is a review for Lesson 11.

I. Answers will vary.

This exercise is a review for Lesson 9.

J. Answers will vary.

This exercise is a review for Lesson 10.

Build Sentences

Lesson 12—Use Variety: Types of Sentences

A. **1.** . declarative   **5.** ? interrogative

  2. . imperative (*or* ! exclamatory)   **6.** . declarative

  3. ! excalmatory   **7.** ! exclamatory

  4. . imperative   **8.** ? interrogative

B. Answers will vary.

C. Answers will vary.

Lesson 13—Use Variety: Sentence Length

A. Answers will vary.

B. Answers will vary.

Lesson 14—Combine Sentences: Compound Sentences

A. Have you ever felt like an alien in your own school? When I first moved here, that's exactly how I felt. <u>It was the middle of the school year, and everyone had already formed groups of friends.</u> They all stared at me as I walked down the hall, like I was an unwelcome intruder from another planet. After a while, things started to get better. <u>People started to call me by my name; they stopped saying, "Hey New Girl."</u> I decided that the best way to make friends was to get involved in activities that I was interested in, so I joined the school <u>band, auditioned for the school play, and tried out for the girls' basketball team.</u> I figured that, among the three groups, there had to be some people who would let an alien sit with them at lunch.

B. Answers will vary.

Lesson 15—Expand Sentences: Adding Details

A. Answers will vary.

B. Answers will vary.

Lesson 16—Edit Sentences: Run-On Sentences

A. I have been playing the violin since I was six it is my favourite thing to do.

We have been rehearsing for weeks this is a major setback.

B. Answers will vary. *Sample answers:*
   1. The soccer coach was very strict. Darren always made sure he arrived at practice on time.
   2. Mikaela has known since she was six that she wants to be a doctor, but I have no idea what career I want.
   3. Peta pressured me to jump off the cliff into the water; I was too scared.

Lesson 17—Know Complete Subjects and Predicates

A. 1. Underline *A heated debate about environmental issues;* circle *started in science class today*
   2. Underline *Many of the city's residents;* circle *have been disappointed with the new mayor's transportation policies*
   3. Underline *One of the students in my gym class;* circle *fainted from heat stroke this afternoon*
   4. Underline *The school band;* circle *will perform at the seniors' residence on Monday*
   5. Underline *Over half of the students in class;* circle *voted in favour of working outside this afternoon*

   6. Underline *Where did you;* circle *put my bag*
   7. Underline *My brother;* circle *taught me the Rabbit Dance for the powwow next week*

B. Answers will vary.

C. Answers will vary.

D. Answers will vary.

Lesson 18—Identify Who or What: Simple Subjects

A. 1. phone   3. food   5. advice
   2. day   4. achievement   6. goal

B. Answers will vary.

C. Answers will vary.

Lesson 19—Identify the Action: Simple Predicates

A. 1. run   4. walked   7. will be going
   2. is escaping   5. applauded   8. have become
   3. am writing   6. is hiring

B. Answers will vary.

C. Answers will vary.

Lesson 20—Identify Who or What: Compound Subjects

A. 1. Underline *aunt, uncle*
   2. There is no compound subject.
   3. Underline *hockey stick, helmet*
   4. Underline *grocery store, pharmacy*

B. 1. Underline *China, India, Thailand;* are
   2. Underline *Serena, Brent;* have
   3. Underline *brother, sister;* bother
   4. Underline *pillow, sleeping bag;* are

C. Answers will vary.

D. Answers will vary.

Lesson 21—Identify the Action: Compound Predicates

A. 1. Underline *grandmother;* circle *lives, drives*
   2. There is no compound predicate.
   3. Underline *girls;* circle *walk, bike*
   4. Underline *father;* circle *gives, is*
   5. Underline *cleaners;* circle *mopped, wiped*
   6. There is no compound predicate.

B. Answers will vary.

C. Answers will vary.

Lesson 22—Understand Compound Subjects and Predicates

A. 1. Underline *looked, smiled*; CP

2. Underline *dishes, laundry*; CS

3. Underline *went, didn't play*; CP

4. Underline *arms, legs*; CS

5. Underline *was getting, wouldn't sleep*; CP

6. Underline *jumped, swam*; CP

B. Answers will vary. *Sample answers*:

1. Louis took out his pencil and started writing.

2. Paolo and Mina follow the lifeguard's instructions closely.

3. The clinic and pharmacy are closed today.

C. Answers will vary.

Lesson 23—Identify Sentence Parts: Direct and Indirect Objects

A. 1. direct object   4. direct object

2. indirect object   5. indirect object

3. indirect object   6. direct object

B. Answers will vary.

Lesson 24—Recognize Independent and Subordinate Clauses

A. 1. Double underline *Before I go for a run*; underline *I always make sure to do some stretches*; circle *Before*

2. Underline *We decided to buy our movie tickets online*; double underline *rather than wait in line when we arrive*; circle *rather than*

3. Double underline *Even though it was raining*; underline *the coach made us do five laps*; circle *Even though*

4. Underline *I'm going over to Aria's house*; double underline *as soon as I finish practising violin*; circle *as soon as*

5. Underline *The plane finally landed*; double underline *after it had circled the airport for twenty minutes*; circle *after*

6. Double underline *Although it is summer*; underline *we are not going to the cottage this year*; circle *Although*

B. Answers will vary.

Lesson 25—Combine Sentences: Complex Sentences

A. 1. My family visited the National Art Gallery in Ottawa when I was seven. *or* When I was seven, my family visited the National Art Gallery in Ottawa.

2. Tamar raced home as soon as school was over. *or* As soon as school was over, Tamar raced home.

3. Our science project, which is on sustainable development, is due on Monday.

B. Answers will vary. Write two complex sentences, using either a conjunction or a relative pronoun to join the subordinate clause to the independent clause.

C. Answers will vary. Write two complex sentences about active living; one sentence should use a conjunction to join the subordinate and independent clauses, and the other sentence should use a relative pronoun.

D. Answers will vary.

Lesson 26—Recognize Clauses: Adjective Clauses

A. 1. when my grandparents visited; N

2. that has chocolate icing and vanilla filling; E

3. who likes mystery novels; E

4. which is next to the fire station; N

B. Answers will vary. Write two sentences about a trip you've taken and use an adjective clause in each sentence.

C. Answers will vary.

Lesson 27—Recognize Clauses: Adverb Clauses

A. 1. because they didn't make it to finals; why?

2. When I got to the store; when?

3. unless I fail the exam; how?

4. where his mom had told him to wait; where?

5. Before I printed my essay; when?

6. so his feet would not get cold; why?

B. Answers will vary.

C. Answers will vary.

Lesson 28—Edit Sentences: Sentence Fragments

A. 1. SF   2. S   3. SF   4. SF

B. Answers will vary. Correct the sentence fragments by adding an independent clause to sentence fragment 1 and adding a noun or pronoun plus the linking verb *was* to sentence fragment 2.

C. Answers will vary.

Lesson 29—Edit Sentences: Comma Splices

A. 1. ✓   2. ✗   3. ✓   4. ✓

B. 1. The kitchen is a mess, so we have to clean up before Mom gets home. *or* The kitchen is a mess. We have to clean up before Mom gets home. *or* The kitchen is a mess; we have to clean up before Mom gets home.

2. Driving to school is faster, but riding a bike is better for your health and the environment. *or* Although driving to school is faster, riding a bike is better for your health and the environment. *or* Driving to school is faster. Riding a bike is better for your health and the environment. *or* Driving to school is faster; riding a bike is better for your health and the environment.

3. I edited my essay, and it had a few spelling mistakes. *or* I edited my essay. It had a few spelling mistakes. *or* I edited my essay; it had a few spelling mistakes.

C. Answers will vary.

Section Review

A. 1. . Imperative   3. ? Interrogative
   2. ! Exclamatory   4. . Declarative

This exercise is a review for Lesson 12.

B. 1. Yes   2. Yes   3. No

This exercise is a review for Lesson 14.

C. Answers will vary.

This exercise is a review for Lesson 15.

D. Answers will vary. *Sample answers:*

1. The test was hard. I studied all night. *or* The test was hard; I studied all night. *or* The test was hard, even though I studied all night.

2. Jay won the race. He hurt his ankle. *or* Jay won the race, but he hurt his ankle.

This exercise is a review for Lesson 16.

E. 1. Underline *car*; circle *has*

2. Underline *buses*; circle *have been arriving*

This exercise is a review for Lessons 18 and 19.

F. 1. will go, swim; CP

2. purse, shoes; CS

3. tomatoes, peppers; CS

4. ran, grabbed; CP

This exercise is a review for Lessons 20–22.

G. 1. Underline *name tags*; circle *guests*

2. Underline *instructions*; circle *Brent*

3. Underline *lecture*; circle *students*

4. Underline *look*; circle *me*

This exercise is a review for Lesson 23.

H. Answers will vary.

This exercise is a review for Lesson 24.

I. 1. who plays violin; E

2. when it was really cold out; N

3. that has shaggy hair and brown and white spots; E

This exercise is a review for Lesson 26.

J. Answers will vary.

1. Correct the sentence fragment by adding a noun or pronoun plus a linking verb to the phrase.

2. Correct the comma splice by making two sentences, by adding either a coordinating conjunction or a subordinating conjunction, or by replacing the comma with a semicolon.

3. Correct the sentence fragment by adding an independent clause. If you place the phrase before the independent clause, you should follow the phrase with a comma.

This exercise is a review for Lessons 28 and 29.

K. Answers will vary.

This exercise is a review for Lessons 13 and 17.

L. Answers will vary.

This exercise is a review for Lesson 25.

Know Capitalization and Punctuation

Lesson 30—Use Capitals: A Variety of Capitalization

A. 1. No; the <u>Most</u> <u>Beautiful</u> <u>Garden</u> Award

2. Yes

3. No; The History of <u>Orchids</u>

4. Yes

B. Sept. 4th

Today I read a poem that reminded me of Greece. "Easter on the Mediterranean Sea" made me think of our outing with Captain Markos. What a beautiful night sky we saw! I have never seen so many constellations: Leo, Virgo, and Ursa Minor were just a few.

C. Answers will vary.

Lesson 31—Know Latin Short Forms: Abbreviations

A. etc., PS, CV, vs., a.m., e.g., c., re

B. **1.** etc.   **2.** e.g.   **3.** i.e.

C. Answers will vary.

Lesson 32—Shorten Business Words: Abbreviations

A. **1.** c   **2.** b

B. "Mr. Longo, what's your <u>ETA</u> at <u>HQ</u>?"

"Sandy, I'm leaving our <u>mfg.</u> <u>dept.</u> now, so I won't be long."

C. Our organization has won an award! Tell all department managers as soon as possible!

D. Answers will vary.

Lesson 33—Separate Adjectives: Commas

A. **1.** Yes; a brown, male dog

2. No

3. No

4. Yes; a hungry, tired team

5. Yes; a filling, healthy meal

6. Yes; fake, cheap merchandise

B. **1.** giant mechanical   **2.** confident, strong

C. Answers will vary. You should have commas in question 2, but not 1 or 3: delicious maple syrup; intelligent, humourous friend OR humourous, intelligent friend; tropical desert island.

D. Answers will vary.

Lesson 34—Punctuate Dialogue: Quotation Marks

A. **1.** '   **2.** "   **3.** '"

B. **1.** Jay said, "I like the story 'Brown Wolf' better than 'To Build a Fire.'"

2. Marcus said, "I think both stories are pretty sad, don't you?"

3. Jay answered, "Yes, but I like that the writer describes dogs so accurately."

C. Answers will vary. *Sample answers*:

Kiara asked, "Have you read 'The Raven'?"

Cedric answered, "I don't know the poem, 'The Raven.'"

Kiara exclaimed, "I love 'The Raven'!"

D. Answers will vary.

Lesson 35—Show Possession: Apostrophes

A. **1.** Jules and Nuala's

2. Jules's and Nuala's

3. classmates' comments

B. **1.** Avery's

2. songs'

3. children's

4. brother's OR brothers' *is acceptable*

5. family's

C. Answers will vary.

Lesson 36—Use Transition Words: Semicolons

A. **1.** Underline *In the early 1900s, much of Canada remained unsettled*; circle *nevertheless*; underline *people came for the opportunities the country offered*.

2. Underline *Cities were growing quickly because of the wave of newcomers*; circle *therefore*; underline *construction jobs were plentiful*.

B. **1.** ; however

2. ; consequently

C. Answers will vary. *Sample answer*:

Many immigrants came to Canada planning to make money and return home; instead, they remained in the country and became part of its identity.

D. Answers will vary. Some sentences should use transition words to link two independent clauses containing related thoughts. Semicolon and comma use should be correct.

E. Answers will vary.

Lesson 37—Introduce a List: Colons

A. **1.** Coach Henley gave us some tips for how to spend the night before the big game: don't practise in case you hurt yourself, eat a healthy dinner, and get a good sleep.

2. I was a bit nervous before the game because I knew several people in the audience: my three cousins, my aunt, and my two best friends.

3. We had a great time yesterday: we ate pizza, had ice cream, and went to the movies.

4. Next year I have three goals: to become a better hitter, to learn how to play shortstop, and to steal a base.

B. **1.** c   **2.** a   **3.** b   **4.** c

C. Answers will vary.

Lesson 38—Add Appositives: Parentheses

A. **1.** Our farmers' market (the largest in the region) runs on Saturdays and Wednesdays.

   2. We buy honey (usually organic) from a local beekeeping operation.

   3. Once we even got some fiddleheads (or young ferns) because they looked so strange!

B. **1.** Yuko and his family have just relocated to the city of Victoria (on Vancouver Island).

   2. Yuko (an avid cyclist) was thrilled to discover that the city has many bike lanes.

C. Answers will vary.

Lesson 39—Guide Readers: A Variety of Punctuation

A. **1.** a fresh, healthy salad *or* a healthy, fresh salad

   2. safe, wide bike routes *or* wide, safe bike routes

   3. warm, windy grasslands *or* windy, warm grasslands

B. **1.** artists'   **2.** photographer's   **3.** children's

C. **1.** People in many parts of the world do not have access to clean water; however, organizations such as Water for People are working for change.

   2. Communities can do many things to become more sustainable: start recycling programs, encourage roof gardens, and use renewable energy sources.

D. War Child (founded in 1999) is dedicated to improving the lives of children.

E. Answers will vary.

F. Answers will vary.

Section Review

A. **1.** Conservation Officer Singh; Parks Canada

   2. The; Fort Steele; British Columbia

   3. The; Wild Horse Creek

   4. Officer Singh; *The Rebirth Fort Steele: Embracing Our Heritage*

   5. Officer Singh's; BC History Award; Sept.

This exercise is a review for Lesson 30.

B. **1.** and so on   **4.** department

   2. for example   **5.** management

   3. that is   **6.** as soon as possible

This exercise is a review for Lessons 31 and 32.

C. **1.** Merida asked the young, friendly waiter for a toasted cheese sandwich.

   2. The energetic, spotless cook delivered the fresh, delicious food personally.

This exercise is a review for Lesson 33.

D. Darla said, "I need a slogan for my election campaign."

"Here's one: 'Vote for Darla—she's darling!'" offered Chris.

"That's terrible!" exclaimed Darla. "'Darling Darla can do the job!'"

Chris commented, "That sounds much better."

This exercise is a review for Lesson 34.

E. **1.** farmers'   **4.** Paula and Patrick's

   2. townspeople's   **5.** twins'

   3. cheese's

This exercise is a review for Lesson 35.

F. **1.** The invention of the telescope has increased our knowledge of the universe; similarly, microscope technology has allowed us to learn more about our own bodies.

   2. Our understanding of cells has led to several breakthroughs in medicine; however, it has also led to the creation of products such as pesticides.

This exercise is a review for Lesson 36.

G. **1.** Yes; the colon follows a complete sentence and introduces a list.

   2. No; the colon introduces a list but comes after a preposition, not a complete sentence.

This exercise is a review for Lesson 37.

H. We met our guide (Santini) at Café Nova (a restaurant in the town square). From there, we travelled by *boita* (a type of boat) to Castle Luffgard. There, we met an *asistente* (an attendant of the emperor), who escorted us into the throne room. Roxelana (the empress) greeted us warmly and offered us a cup of Dragon Well, which is a rare green tea.

This exercise is a review for Lesson 38.

I. Answers will vary.

This exercise is a review for Lessons 37, 38, and 39.

J. Answers will vary.

This exercise is a review for Lessons 34, 35, and 39.

Grasp Grammar and Usage

Lesson 40—Name the Person, Place, Thing, or Idea: Nouns

A. **1.** To raise <u>money</u> for our <u>foster child</u>, our <u>school</u> held an <u>auction</u> of <u>artwork</u> created by <u>students</u>.

   2. <u>WE Charity</u> is an <u>organization</u> that began in <u>Canada</u> and empowers <u>youth</u> around the <u>world</u>.

3. Last <u>summer</u>, <u>Aunt Monique</u> volunteered as a <u>house-builder</u> for a local <u>charity</u>.

4. For the <u>Brookton Science Fair</u>, <u>Jaya</u> and <u>Wes</u> created a simple <u>pump</u> for <u>use</u> in <u>communities</u> that lack clean <u>water</u>.

5. Our <u>class</u> uses various <u>media</u> to stay aware of international <u>issues</u> and <u>events</u>.

6. <u>People</u> in our former <u>village</u> lost their <u>homes</u> in the recent <u>earthquake</u>.

B.
1. COM	**4.** COM	**7.** COL
2. COM	**5.** COL	**8.** COL
3. PR	**6.** PR	**9.** PR

C.
1. drive-in	**3.** software	**5.** washing machine
2. post office	**4.** baseball	

D. Answers will vary.

E. Answers will vary.

Lesson 41—Show Ownership: Singular Possessive Nouns

A.
1. the duchess's marriage
2. the sandwich's fillings
3. the computer's software
4. the fox's habitat

B.
1. community's	**3.** Travis's	**5.** compass's
2. chief's	**4.** area's	

C. Answers will vary, but the form should be *business's*.

D. Answers will vary.

Lesson 42—Show Ownership: Plural Possessive Nouns

A. **1.** S **2.** P **3.** P **4.** P

B. Answers will vary. Use the following forms logically in a sentence:
1. foxes' 2. studios' 3. tomatoes'

C.
1. The seagulls' prey includes fish, worms, insects, and reptiles.
2. These areas' mountains are volcanic.

D. Answers will vary.

Lesson 43—Make Irregular Plural Nouns Possessive

A.
1. women's	**3.** teeth's	**5.** sheep's
2. feet's	**4.** cacti's	

B. Answers will vary. Use the following forms logically in a sentence:
1. men's 2. women's 3. children's

C. Answers will vary.

D. Answers will vary.

Lesson 44—Use Concrete and Abstract Nouns

A.
1. C	**3.** A	**5.** A	**7.** A
2. A	**4.** C	**6.** C	**8.** C

B.
1. Underline *friend, daycare, neighbourhood*; circle *friendship*
2. Underline *sister, college, buildings, gardens, roofs, food*; circle *ecology*
3. Underline *bus, students, city, guide*; circle *efforts, sustainability*
4. Underline *Canadians, community, citizens*; circle *right*

C. Answers will vary.

D. Answers will vary.

Lesson 45—Identify a Variety of Verbs

A.
1. Underline *was;* a
2. Underline *sounds;* b
3. Underline *looked;* b

B.
1. action	**3.** linking	**5.** action
2. auxiliary	**4.** phrasal	

C. Answers will vary. *Sample answers*:
1. pounced on its prey
2. are heading home
3. tastes delicious
4. my cousin showed up

D. Answers will vary.

Lesson 46—Provide More Information: Verb Phrases

A.
1. was wearing	**4.** has become
2. may be hosting	**5.** can remember
3. was trembling	

B. Answers will vary. Sentences should use each verb phrase in a way that makes sense.

C. Answers will vary. Verb phrases should fit logically with the rest of the sentence. For #1, the verb phrase should be in the future tense. For #2, the verb phrase should be in the past tense. For #3, the verb phrase could be in the present or past tense.

D. Answers will vary.

Lesson 47—Show When an Action Happens: Verb Tenses

A.
1. past progressive	**4.** simple past
2. simple future	**5.** simple present
3. present progressive	

B. 1. babysit; am babysitting   **4.** was studying

  2. will give   **5.** chose; am choosing; will choose

  3. interviewed; had interviewed   **6.** hit; was hitting

C. Answers will vary. The verb forms should be
  1. am/is/are growing   **2.** was/were trying

D. Answers will vary. The first paragraph should be written in the simple present tense. The second paragraph should be written in one of the following tenses: present progressive, simple past, past progressive, or simple future tense.

E. Answers will vary.

Lesson 48 — Make the Past Tense: Irregular Verbs

A. 1. gave   **3.** saw   **5.** drank

  2. cost   **4.** swung

B. 1. stood   **2.** became   **3.** hit   **4.** broke

C. Answers will vary.

Lesson 49 — Use Present Perfect and Past Perfect Tenses

A. 1. b   **2.** a   **3.** c   **4.** a   **5.** c

B. 1. have learned – PrP

  2. has shown – PrP

  3. had rehearsed – PP

  4. had conducted – PP

  5. had practised – PP

  6. have eaten – PrP

C. Answers will vary. Your sentences will use the words *forgot, understood,* and *bought.*

Lesson 50 — Match the Numbers: Subject–Verb Agreement

A. 1. contains   **3.** is planning   **5.** has

  2. are staying   **4.** are

B. 1. Underline *Minerals and forests*; circle *are*; P

  2. Underline *bowl*; circle *makes*; S

  3. Underline *someone*; circle *is lifting*; S

  4. Underline *determination and skill*; circle *inspire*; P

  5. Underline *couple*; circle *celebrates*; S

  6. Underline *Both*; circle *are*; P

C. Answers will vary. #1 requires a plural verb; #2 requires a singular verb; #3 requires a singular verb.

D. Concussions <u>are</u> a type of brain injury that can result from hits to the head. If someone who <u>has been</u> hit in the head <u>experiences</u> blurred vision, confusion, or severe headache, he or she should be taken to the emergency department. Slurred speech and dizziness <u>are</u> other possible signs of concussion. If you play team sports, make sure your coaches <u>know</u> the signs of concussion. Your team, as a whole, <u>needs</u> to pay attention to any hits players <u>receive</u>. Share information about concussions. For example, "Protecting Brains," a safety video I made with my friend, <u>was</u> shown to my whole school.

Lesson 51 — Match the Subject: Linking Verbs

A. 1. osprey – is   **2.** event – is   **3.** monuments – are
  4. skill and guidance – have been   **5.** beads – are
  6. gift – is   **7.** Food and warmth – were

B. Answers will vary. The verb for #1 should be plural and the verb for #2 should be singular.

C. Answers will vary.

Lesson 52 — Understand Active and Passive Voice

A. 1. Underline *student*; circle *was introduced*

  2. Underline *Hailey*; circle *tossed*

  3. Underline *parents*; circle *laughed*

  4. Underline *sister*; circle *is being awarded*

  5. Underline *Karif*; circle *made*

  6. Underline *silo and barns*; circle *were damaged*

  7. Underline *play*; circle *will be performed*

B. 1. Active   **3.** Active   **5.** Active

  2. Passive   **4.** Passive

C. 1. An archaeologist discovered an interesting artifact yesterday. (Note that the placement of *yesterday* may vary.)

  2. The class chose Braden as spokesperson.

  3. Our science class will conduct buoyancy experiments next week. (Note the placement of *next week* may vary.)

  4. The committee chose a new logo.

D. Answers will vary.

E. Answers will vary.

Lesson 53 — Replace Subject Nouns: Subject Pronouns

A. 1. They   **2.** It   **3.** We   **4.** You

B. 1. You   **2.** we   **3.** It   **4.** he   **5.** they

C. Answers will vary, but the subject pronoun for #1 should be *They*, and the subject pronoun for #2 should be *It*.

Lesson 54—Replace Object Nouns: Object Pronouns

A. 1. Underline *it*; circle *yoga*

2. Underline *them*; circle *sunscreen and hat*

3. Underline *us*; circle *my brother and me*

4. Underline *her*; circle *sister*

5. Underline *them*; circle *war veterans*

B. 1. me   2. it   3. us   4. us   5. him

C. Answers will vary.

Lesson 55—Show Ownership: Possessive Pronouns

A. 1. mine   3. theirs   5. his

2. yours   4. ours

B. 1. mine   3. yours   5. ours

2. hers   4. theirs

C. 1. Answers will vary.

Lesson 56—Use Indefinite Pronouns

A. 1. fewer   3. others   5. everyone

2. several   4. some

B. 1. All – are going   3. any – are   5. anything – makes

2. Both – are   4. more – was

C. Answers will vary.

Lesson 57—Describe Nouns: Relative Pronouns

A. 1. that Sasha made – that

2. who knew my great-grandmother – who

3. whose name is Abby – whose

4. who fixed our car – who

5. which is on the fifth floor – which

6. that she likes best – that

B. 1. who   4. which   7. whose

2. whose   5. that

3. who   6. which

Lesson 58—Make Pronouns and Antecedents Agree

A. 1. Underline *pen*; circle *it*

2. Underline *cats*; circle *themselves*

3. Underline *Kyra and Shane*; circle *they*

4. Underline *Zohar*; circle *his*

5. Underline *girl*; circle *hers*

6. Underline *You and Riley*; circle *you*

B. 1. myself   4. yours   7. them

2. it   5. we   8. us

3. his   6. themselves

Lesson 59—Use a Variety of Pronouns and Antecedents

A. 1. she   4. many   7. which

2. his   5. ourselves

3. them   6. those

B. 1. himself   3. it   5. These

2. some   4. you

C. When people conduct science experiments, **they** should wear protective gear. (*or* When **you** conduct science experiments, *you* should wear protective gear.)

Lesson 60—Write Descriptive Words: Adjectives

A. 1. that   2. Those   3. these

B. 1. his   2. her   3. my

C. 1. What   2. Whose   3. Which

D. 1. This, various, government, clean

2. Whose, safety, storage, power

3. Arctic, their, large, furry

E. Answers will vary. Use two adjectives that make sense with the context of the provided sentence. *Sample answers*:

1. cheering, adoring   4. bustling, art

2. large, funny   5. small, multicultural

3. happy, euphoric

F. Answers will vary.

Lesson 61—Make Comparisons: Adjectives

A. 1. least certain   4. mightiest

2. bluer   5. smaller

3. more famous   6. sadder

B. 1. redder   4. more expensive

2. quieter   5. more confused

3. friendliest

C. Answers will vary.

Lesson 62—Describe Actions: Adverbs

A. 1. carefully, confidently

2. occasionally, usually, away

3. very, briskly, quickly, inside

4. hard, soon, dangerously

B. 1. Underline *constantly and endlessly*; circle *pass*

    2. Underline *very often*; circle *used*

    3. Underline *slowly and painfully*; circle *limped*

C. Answers will vary, but you should choose adverbs that describe the action logically and add interest to the sentences.

Lesson 63—Write Descriptively: Adjectives and Adverbs

A. 1. ADJ   **2.** ADV   **3.** ADJ   **4.** ADJ

B. 1. differently   **3.** sincerely

    2. well   **4.** immaturely

C. Answers will vary.

Lesson 64—Show Relationships: Prepositions

A. 1. Excluding, of, over

    2. For, down, from, to

    3. inside, of, by

    4. outside, around, from, past

B. 1. along   **3.** toward   **5.** behind

    2. for   **4.** beyond

C. Answers will vary.

D. Answers will vary.

Lesson 65—Describe a Noun: Prepositional Phrases

A. 1. They walked <u>along the waterfront</u> <u>until sunset</u> and then hopped <u>onto a bus</u> <u>for home</u>.

    2. <u>Near our farm</u>, <u>beyond the wheat fields</u>, stands a small forest <u>of mainly deciduous trees</u>.

    3. <u>Through our research</u>, we are learning <u>about sustainability</u> <u>in human communities</u>.

    4. <u>During our buoyancy experiment</u> <u>in science class</u>, Madeline accidentally dropped a big rock <u>into the water</u>, <u>from quite a height</u>—nobody was dry <u>until the end</u> <u>of the next class</u>.

    5. Tariq is going <u>to the Laurentians</u> <u>in Québec</u> <u>for a ski trip</u> and to visit family.

    6. <u>At the Teslin Tlingit Heritage Centre</u>, a celebration <u>of Tlingit culture</u> takes place biennially, <u>in the summer</u>.

B. Answers will vary. Use prepositional phrases found within the lesson or think of others. Your phrases must start with a preposition, and not a conjunction.

Lesson 66—Describe a Noun: Participle Phrases

A. 1. participle phrase: Breathing deeply; noun: competitor

    2. participle phrase: gathered for the yard sale; noun: items

    3. participle phrase: Shaken by his fall; noun: cyclist

B. Answers will vary. The participle phrase should agree with the noun it modifies and work logically with the sentence.

C. Answers will vary. If you place the participle phrase at the beginning of the sentence, you should follow it with a comma. If you place the participle phrase after the noun and it is restrictive, there should be no comma. The participle phrase should agree with the noun it modifies.

Lesson 67—Be Clear: Misplaced Modifiers

A. 1. A firefighter <u>in full uniform</u> was rescuing a cat. Circle *firefighter*

    2. The store clerk <u>kindly</u> apologized for the mistake he made. Circle *apologized*

    3. We feel sorry for our neighbour's <u>barking</u> dog. Circle *dog*

    4. <u>In the canoe</u>, Dad said that we could roast marshmallows later. Circle *said*

Note that placement of the modifiers may vary, but they should be placed closer to the word they modify.

B. 1. She nearly missed her bus ten times.

    2. Only Kiera liked the dessert.

C. Answers will vary.

Lesson 68—Be Clear: Misplaced and Dangling Modifiers

A. 1. Sketching in the art studio, they saw a deer and her two fawns.

    2. We watched the snapping turtle slowly emerging from the pond scum.

    3. The chef served raspberries and cream on a thin layer of chocolate biscuit.

Note, for sentence #1, place a comma after the participle phrase because it appears at the beginning of the sentence.

B. Answers will vary. You will need to add and/or change the order of words. *Sample answers*:

    1. As she was waving goodbye at the airport, her suitcase was stolen.

    2. Diving off the high board, he thought Earth seemed to stop moving.

    3. As they were soaking up the warm October sun, their worries were forgotten.

Lesson 69—Use Joining Words: Conjunctions

A. **1.** Whenever – S   **4.** Although – S

   2. Because – S   **5.** yet – C

   3. and – C

B. Answers will vary.

C. Answers will vary.

D. Answers will vary.

Lesson 70: Express Emotions: Interjections

A. **1.** What?   **3.** Ugh!   **5.** Really?

   2. No,   **4.** Oh yeah,   **6.** Aww,

Note that, for punctuation, answers may vary. In some cases, you can use clues from the sentence's end punctuation and capitalization of the word following the interjection.

B. Answers will vary. Choose logical interjections for the sentences and use correct and appropriate punctuation.

C. Answers will vary. Write endings that relate logically to the interjection and the punctuation that follows it.

D. Answers will vary.

Lesson 71—Be Careful: Avoid Double Negatives

A. **1.** I have not got *any*.

   2. We don't need *any* help.

   3. Don't tell *anybody*.

   4. I can't find my pen *anywhere*.

   5. She won't find *anything*.

   6. Do not call me *anymore*.

B. **1.** can   **3.** will   **5.** have

   2. any   **4.** anywhere   **6.** do

C. Answers will vary.

Section Review

A. **1.** Auntie Asha, vice-principal, school, cousins, Calgary

   2. Volunteers, neighbourhood, books, communities

   3. sister, swimming pool, maintenance, month

   4. town, fireworks, Canada Day, dogs, distress

   5. Canadian Paralympic Committee, website, information, Parasport

This exercise is a review for Lesson 40.

B. Answers will vary.

This exercise is a review for Lesson 40.

C. **1.** action   **3.** phrasal   **5.** auxiliary

   2. linking   **4.** action

This exercise is a review for Lesson 45.

D. **1.** will begin   **3.** saw   **5.** was skateboarding

   2. wrote   **4.** brought

This exercise is a review for Lessons 47 and 48.

E. **1.** Underline "*Polar Ice-Caps*"; circle *is*; S

   2. Underline *Someone*; circle *is calling*; S

   3. Underline *Recycling and composting*; circle *are*; P

   4. Underline *Many*; circle *have seen*; P

This exercise is a review for Lessons 50 and 51.

F. **1.** whose   **2.** who   **3.** which   **4.** that

This exercise is a review for Lesson 57.

G. **1.** Circle *it*; underline *ball*

   2. Circle *yourself*; underline *You*

   3. Circle *they*; underline *Amy and LaShawn*

   4. Circle *them*; underline *forest fires*

   5. Circle *he*; underline *Uncle Marco*

This exercise is a review for Lessons 58 and 59.

H. **1.** adverb   **3.** adverb   **5.** adjective

   2. adjective   **4.** adverb

This exercise is a review for Lessons 62 and 63.

I. Answers will vary. Add adjectives and adverbs to each sentence to make them more descriptive.

This exercise is a review for Lessons 62 and 63.

J. **1.** off the couch; in the nice sunshine

   2. By sheer bad luck; onto my head; during our presentation

   3. In a few weeks; along the ski trails; of Jasper, Alberta

This exercise is a review for Lessons 64 and 65.

K. **1.** anything   **2.** any   **3.** anywhere

This exercise is a review for Lesson 71.

L. Answers will vary.

This exercise is a review for Lessons 60, 61, 62, 63, 65, and 70.

M. Answers will vary.

This exercise is a review for Lesson 69.

Craft and Compose

Lesson 72—Use Your Knowledge: Choosing a Topic

A. Answers will vary.

B. Answers will vary.

C. Answers will vary.

Lesson 73—Consider Purpose and Audience

A. 1. b   **2.** a

Explanations will vary, but you should cite reasons related to each audience's background knowledge about the topic.

B. Answers will vary.

Lesson 74—Formulate a Thesis: Topic Versus Thesis

A. 1. a   **2.** b

B. Answers will vary. You should write a thesis on the topic of the last day of school. The topic and your view of the topic should be evident in the thesis.

Lesson 75—Create a Senses Chart: Organizing Ideas

A. **1.** sound (hear)

2. taste or smell or sight (see)

3. touch (feel) or sight (see)

4. smell or sight (see)

5. touch (feel)

6. taste or smell or sight (see)

7. sight (see) or sound (hear) or smell

8. sound (hear)

B. Answers will vary.

C. Answers will vary.

Lesson 76—Write What and Why: Strong Openings

A. Answers will vary.

B. Answers will vary.

C. Answers will vary.

Lesson 77—Find Strengths and Weaknesses: Writing Details

A. **1.** Ashish's strengths: determined   creative

Ashish's weaknesses: nervous   insecure

2. Autumn's strengths: calm   confident

Autumn's weaknesses: presumptuous   lazy

B. Answers will vary.

C. Answers will vary.

Lesson 78—Use Your Senses: Supporting Details

A. 1. a   **2.** b   **3.** a

B. Answers will vary. You should write a main idea and two supporting details about a place that inspires you.

C. Answers will vary.

Lesson 79—Order by Time: Arranging Details

A. 1. 3   **2.** 1   **3.** 4   **4.** 5   **5.** 2

B. Answers will vary.

C. Answers will vary.

Lesson 80—Show Character and Situation: Writing Dialogue

A. Ben: nervous; Mr. Ng: concerned

B. Answers will vary.

C. Answers will vary.

Lesson 81—Make Language Precise: Sensory Words

A. Answers will vary. Rewrite the sentences by replacing the one-word descriptions with sensory words.

B. Answers will vary.

Lesson 82—Restate What and Why: Strong Conclusions

A. Answers will vary. Write sentences explaining the *what* and *why* in the conclusions provided. *Sample answers*:

1. What: you need to look closely at art; Why: you see details you might have missed.

2. What: volunteering; Why: It is a worthwhile experience.

B. Answers will vary.

C. Answers will vary.

Lesson 83—Catch Your Readers' Attention: Effective Titles

A. Answers will vary.

B. Answers will vary.

Lesson 84—Improve Word Choice and Spelling: Revising

A. **1.** rain, their

2. excitement, board

3. pain, soccer

4. runner, breath

B. Answers will vary.

C. Answers will vary. *Sample answers*:

  1. Isaac and Michael went home early *from the party* because *Michael ate too much ice cream* and was feeling sick.

  2. The man *across the street* walks his *beagle* every day, even when the weather is *cold* or *stormy*.

  3. *Before we reached the end of the street*, we had to turn around because I left my bag *on the doorstep*.

D. Answers will vary.

Lesson 85—Correct Sentences: Editing

A. Answers will vary. *Sample answers*:

  1. The wind turbines made a lot of noise, *and* (or *so*) many local residents complained.

  2. *The women* (or any other reasonable noun) stared at the painting for over ten minutes.

  3. *It was* (or any other reasonable noun or pronoun + linking verb) hidden at the bottom of my backpack under all the school books. Or

  Hidden at the bottom of my backpack under all the school books, *my wallet was safe.* (or any other independent clause)

  4. They dug up the front yard to put in a vegetable garden, *but* (or *and*) it was hard work. Or

  They dug up the front yard to put in a vegetable garden. *It* was hard work.

  5. The dark clouds were moving closer to the baseball field, *yet* (or *but, and*) the team kept playing. Or

  The dark clouds were moving closer to the baseball field. *The* team kept playing.

B. Answers will vary. *Sample answer*:

  Running a 5 km race is hard work, but the feeling of accomplishment makes it worth it. I had been training for months, *and* I knew I was ready. On the day of the race, I was nervous. *I was* looking at the other runners. They looked so strong and confident. I imagined them racing past me as I huffed and puffed in last place. When the race started, all those thoughts disappeared. *I* focused on my breathing, on keeping a steady pace, and on finishing the race.

C. Answers will vary.

Section Review

A. Answers will vary.

  This exercise is a review for Lesson 72.

B. Answers will vary.

  This exercise is a review for Lesson 73.

C. Answers will vary.

  This exercise is a review for Lesson 74.

D. Answers will vary.

  This exercise is a review for Lesson 75.

E. Answers will vary.

  This exercise is a review for Lesson 76.

F. Jesse's strengths: **3.** reliable **4.** compassionate

  This exercise is a review for Lesson 77.

G. **1.** 3 **2.** 1 **3.** 2 **4.** 4

  Underline *when, then,* and *soon*

  This exercise is a review for Lesson 79.

H. Answers will vary.

  This exercise is a review for Lessons 81 and 84.

I. Answers will vary. *Sample answers*:

  1. My grandmother likes flowers, *and* she works in her garden every day. *Or*

  My grandmother likes flowers. *She* works in her garden every day.

  2. *The crow* soared over the trees and flew away.

  This exercise is a review for Lesson 85.

J. Answers will vary.

  This exercise is a review for Lessons 76, 78, 82, and 83.

K. Answers will vary.

  This exercise is a review for Lessons 80 and 84.

Develop Research Skills

Lesson 86—Think Critically: Inquiry Questions

A. **1.** Ineffective. Answers will vary. You may note that the question has a simple answer, and it does not encourage critical thinking. You may also already know how to make pancakes.

  2. Effective. Answers will vary. You may note that the question is open-ended, focused, debatable, and can be answered by research.

B. Answers will vary. You may note that the question has too simple an answer. You should write an inquiry question that meets the criteria listed in the box at the top of the page.

Lesson 87—Find Synonyms and Antonyms: Researching Words

A. **1.** reduce, diminish   **3.** deficiency, scarcity

     2. abettor, collaborator   **4.** lively, active

B. Answers will vary. *Sample answers*:

1. mandatory
2. intentional
3. vertical
4. peace
5. lenient

C. Answers will vary. *Sample answers*: Formal synonyms: serene, tranquil, relaxed, quiet, still; Informal synonyms: chill, cool, still, quiet; Formal antonyms: nervous, agitated, excited, frenzied, turbulent; Informal antonyms: crazy, wavy, hyper, active, uncool.

D. Answers will vary.

Lesson 88—Choose Resources: Library Research

A. Answers will vary. *Sample answers*:

1. an online encyclopedia; an online encyclopedia will give facts about a general topic like the fur trade.
2. manual; a manual will give details about how something works.
3. print or online newspaper; a newspaper is best because the earthquake is a current event.

B. Answers will vary. *Sample answers*:

1. print or online newspaper
2. websites
3. manual

C. Answers will vary.

Lesson 89—Conduct Online Research: Keywords

A. c

B. Answers will vary. *Sample answers*:

1. CPR courses Yellowknife
2. Water for people focus
3. media influence teen understanding healthy eating

C. Answers will vary.

D. Answers will vary.

E. Keyword search words will vary. You should first find John A. Macdonald's birth date and then find an 1825 calendar.

Answer to challenge: Tuesday

Lesson 90—Consider Bias: Primary and Secondary Sources

A. 1. Answers will vary. *Sample answer*: First-hand accounts of specific events are based on one's experiences. A person experiencing war will be able to describe their feelings and understandings, but may have difficulty knowing, appreciating, or thinking about the perspectives of people on the opposite side.

2. Answers will vary. *Sample answer*: History texts are often created by compiling information from a variety of primary and secondary sources. If all of these sources are taken from people on one side of the conflict, or are taken from sources written in a language typically spoken by people on one side of the conflict, they may result in a one-sided or unbalanced view of events.

3. Answers will vary. *Sample answer*: The best way to fully understand any issue or topic is to look for and consider all perspectives.

B. Answers will vary.

Lesson 91— Spot Hoaxes: Online Sources

A. You should select either a or b.

B. Answers will vary.

C. Answers will vary. *Sample answer*:

1. It's very hard to lose 20 lbs in one week; banana peel vitamins are uncommon if not unheard of; people need to exercise and eat well to lose weight, and it takes longer.
2. There are no sticky note crops.

D. Answers will vary.

Lesson 92—Investigate Copyright: Plagiarism

A. 1. False   2. True   3. False

B. Answers will vary. Ensure that you write the definitions in your own words, rather than copying directly from the box at the top of the page.

C. Answers will vary.

Lesson 93—In-Text Citations: Citing Research

A. False. Answers will vary. *Sample answer*: Whenever you summarize, paraphrase, or quote a source, you need to provide a citation both within the text and in a bibliography or works cited page.

Ensure you understand that there are multiple ways to include citations in texts (in-text citations, endnotes, footnotes), and that the method is often dictated by the subject discipline.

B. Answers will vary. *Sample answer*:

Potter points out that, since it does not involve words, body language such as posture and facial expressions is a form of "nonverbal" communication (82).

C. Answers will vary.

Lesson 94—Maintain a Citations List: Research Notes

A. 1. title of page, title of website, date site was created or last updated, date you visited site, possibly URL

2. Maxime can use her citations list to direct her back to the original source, to check and make sense of the information provided.

B. Answers will vary. You may mention that having the resources at hand will make it easier to embed citations or write footnotes or endnotes, and that having the details in a working copy to begin with will make it easier to put together a final works cited page. You may also mention that it will be easier to keep track of where your research came from, and to go back to it to check information if needed.

C. Answers will vary. You should number the sources in your working citations list to match the number in your notes. If necessary, review proper formatting of bibliographical entries appropriate for your subject area (e.g., MLA, Chicago style).

D. Answers will vary.

Lesson 95—Cite Your Sources: Paraphrasing and Quoting

A. Answers will vary. *Sample answers*:

1. Due to extensive fishing and overseas trade in the 1850s, about 350 ships per year were built in the Maritime colonies during this time period.

2. English and French are Canada's official languages, while 60 Indigenous languages and 100 other languages are also spoken.

B. Answers will vary. You should mention that crediting the source directly within the report makes it clear where the information came from, and that having the full citation in the bibliography or works cited page makes it easier for readers to find the original source, should they need it.

C. Answers will vary. You should identify the main idea, select a quote, and write point-form notes.

D. Answers will vary. You should write a paragraph based on your notes. You should use a quote and incorporate an in-text citation.

Section Review

A. 1. E. Explanations will vary. You may note that the question is open-ended, focused, debatable, and researchable.

2. I. Explanations will vary. You may note that the question is not open-ended and has a simple answer.

This exercise is a review for Lesson 86.

B. 1. assortment, variety   3. disparaging, defamatory

2. pessimism, despair

This exercise is a review for Lesson 87.

C. Answers will vary. *Sample answers*:

1. help, aid, support

2. gather, collect

3. placid, calm

This exercise is a review for Lesson 87.

D. Answers will vary.

This exercise is a review for Lesson 88.

E. Answers will vary. You should discover that the prime minister was Lester B. Pearson, who was born in Newtonbrook (now Toronto), Ontario.

This exercise is a review for Lesson 89.

F. Answers will vary. You should note that the best way to fully understand any issue or topic is to look for and consider all perspectives. Looking for bias helps determine whether all perspectives have been presented.

This exercise is a review for Lesson 90.

G. Answers will vary. *Sample answers*:

1. Dinosaurs are extinct, and no eggs could survive thousands of years and hatch.

2. Ice cream would melt if roasted or sun-dried.

This exercise is a review for Lesson 91.

H. Answers will vary. *Sample answers*:

1. Read the Creative Commons licence and ensure that you use the material as directed by the creator; credit the creator of the photo in your report.

2. Write the notes in your own words (paraphrase), and credit the source.

This exercise is a review for Lesson 92.

I. Answers will vary.

This exercise is a review for Lessons 94 and 95.

J. Answers will vary.

This exercise is a review for Lessons 93 and 95.

K. Answers will vary.

This exercise is a review for Lessons 94 and 95.

L. Answers will vary.

This exercise is a review for Lessons 93 and 95.

STORY MAP

Characters	Setting
Problem	**Solution**

Beginning	Middle	End

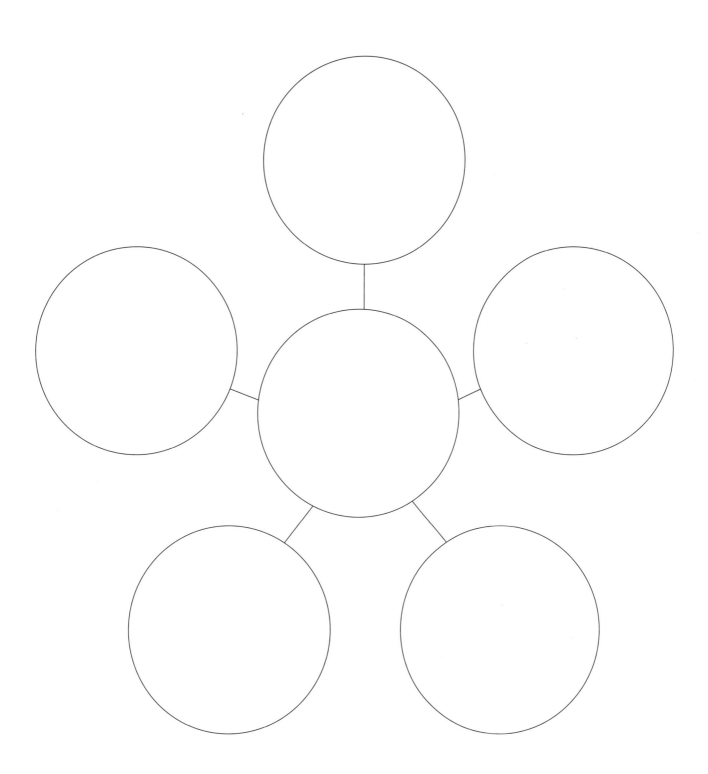

5W WEB

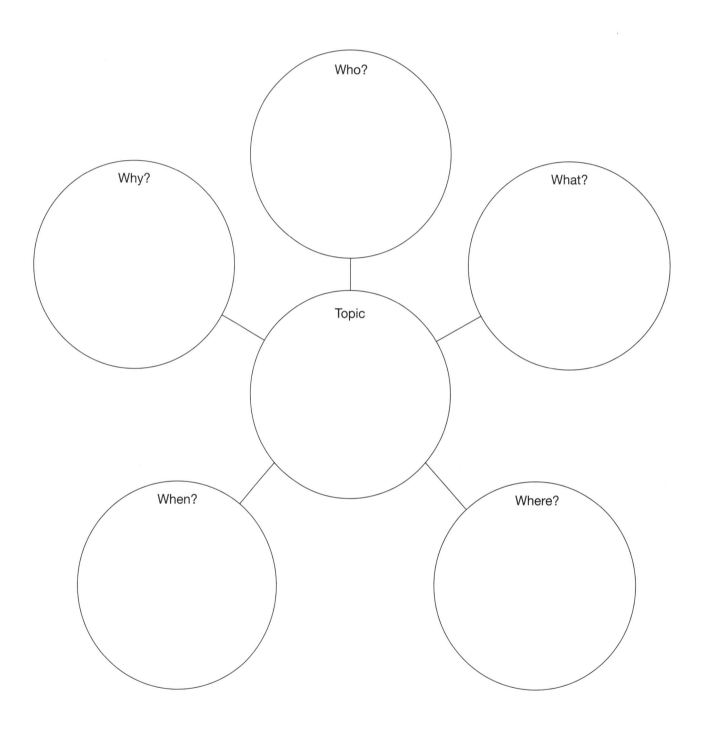

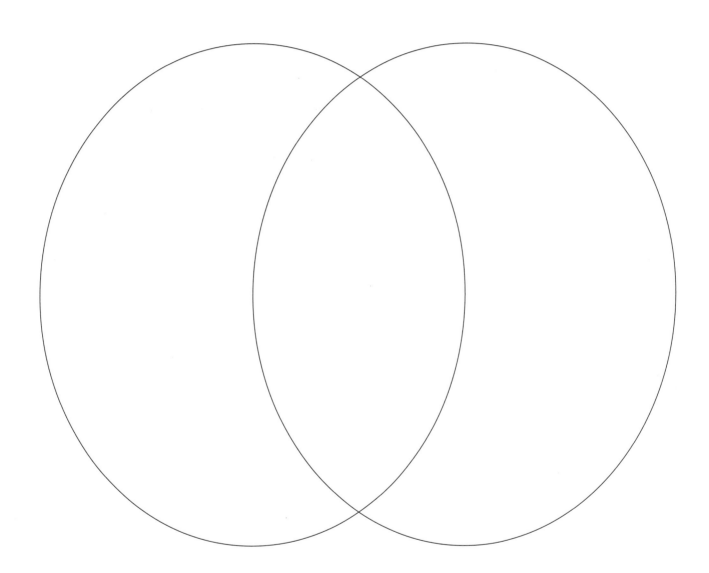

INDEX